AWESOME
BIBLE
ACTIVITIES

COLLECTIONS 3 AND 4

Written by Vickie Save
Illustrated by Ken Save

BARBOUR
PUBLISHING, INC.
Uhrichsville, Ohio

ISBN 1-57748-356-1

Published by Barbour Publishing, Inc., P.O. Box 719, Uhrichsville, Ohio 44683
http://www.barbourbooks.com

Member of the
Evangelical Christian
Publishers Association

Printed in the United States of America.

COLOR THE PICTURE

GOD IS THE CREATOR

FINISH THE VERSES

FINISH THE VERSES BY MATCHING THEM WITH THE PHRASES ON THE FOLLOWING PAGE.

1. "IN THE BEGINNING GOD CREATED...

_____

GENESIS 1:1

2. "AND GOD SAID, 'LET THERE BE LIGHT...'

_____

GENESIS 1:3

3. "AND GOD SAID, ' LET THERE BE AN EXPANSE BETWEEN...

_____

GENESIS 1:6

4. "SO GOD MADE AN EXPANSE AND SEPARATED...

_____

GENESIS 1:7

5. "AND IT WAS SO. GOD CALLED THE...

_____

GENESIS 1:8

6. "AND GOD SAID. 'LET THE WATER UNDER THE SKY...

_____

GENESIS 1:9

ANSWERS FOR THE PREVIOUS PAGE.

-THE HEAVENS AND THE EARTH."

-AND THERE WAS LIGHT."

-THE WATERS TO SEPARATE WATER FROM
  WATER.'"

-THE WATER UNDER THE EXPANSE FROM THE
  WATER ABOVE IT."

-EXPANSE 'SKY'."

-BE GATHERED TO ONE PLACE AND LET DRY
  GROUND APPEAR.'"

3

FINISH THE VERSE

TO FIND OUT WHAT THE VERSE BELOW SAYS, FILL
IN THE BLANKS. ALL THE CONSONANTS ARE THERE,
SO ALL YOU NEED TO DO IS ADD THE VOWELS.

VOWELS: A E I O U

"G __ D C __ LL __ D TH __ DRY

GR __ __ ND 'L __ ND' __ ND TH __

G __ TH __ R __ D W __ T __ RS H __

C __ LL __ D 'S __ __ S'. __ ND G __ D

S __ W TH __ T __ T W __ S

G __ __ D."

GENESIS 1:10

4

FILL IN THE BLANKS

WORD LIST:

VEGETATION   SEED
LAND   TREES
THEIR   KINDS
PLANTS   FRUIT

"THEN GOD SAID, ' LET THE __ __ __ __

PRODUCE __ __ __ __ __ __ __ __ __ __ :

SEED-BEARING __ __ __ __ __ __ AND

__ __ __ __ __ ON THE LAND THAT BEAR

__ __ __ __ __ WITH __ __ __ __ IN IT,

ACCORDING TO __ __ __ __ __ VARIOUS

KINDS.' "

GENESIS 1:11

5

TWICE THE FUN

UNSCRAMBLE THE UNDERLINED WORD IN EACH VERSE. THEN, ON THE OPPOSITE PAGE, FIND AND CIRCLE IT IN THE WORD SEARCH PUZZLE.

1. "AND GOD SAID, 'LET THERE BE ILHGTS IN THE EXPANSE OF THE SKY TO SEPARATE THE AYD FROM HTGIN.'

   GENESIS 1:14

2. "OGD MADE TWO GREAT LIGHTS—THE GREATER LIGHT TO GOVERN THE DAY AND THE LESSER LIGHT TO GOVERN THE NIGHT. HE ALSO MADE THE SSRAT."

   GENESIS 1:16

3. "SO GOD CREATED THE GREAT CREATURES OF THE ESA AND EVERY GLINVI AND GMNOVI THING WITH WHICH THE WATER TEAMS, ACCORDING TO THEIR KINDS, AND EVERY WINGED DBRI ACCORDING TO ITS DKNI."

   GENESIS 1:21

6

```
L  M  I  N  I  G  H  T
I  Y  K  E  S  F  K  Z
G  B  M  O  V  I  N  G
H  A  S  N  N  G  C  U
T  R  E  D  P  D  A  Y
S  T  A  R  S  O  U  O
L  I  V  I  N  G  I  O
F  E  Y  B  J  K  S  W
```

HI!

ZANY CODE BUSTER

USE THE CODE CHART BELOW TO DECODE THE MYSTERY VERSE.

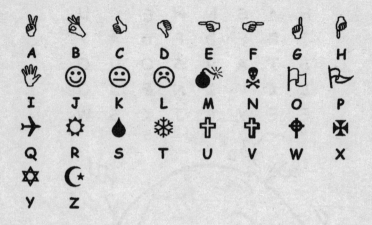

CONT'D ON THE NEXT PAGE...

GENESIS 1:24

9

ZANY CODE BUSTER

TO DECODE THIS MYSTERY VERSE, LOOK AT EACH LETTER AND WRITE THE ONE THAT COMES <u>BEFORE</u> IT IN THE ALPHABET.

A B C D E F G H I J K L M N O P Q R
S T U V W X Y X

"
U I F O   H P E

T B J E'   M F U

V T   N B L F

N B O   J O

P V S   P X O

J N B H F'   J O

CONT'D ON THE NEXT PAGE...

<u> </u> <u> </u> <u> </u>   <u> </u> <u> </u> <u> </u> <u> </u>-
P   V   S   M   J   L   F

<u> </u> <u> </u> <u> </u> <u> </u>."
O   F   T   T

GENESIS 1:26

OUCH!

11

CODE BUSTER

USE THE CODE CHART BELOW TO COMPLETE THE VERSE. CHOOSE FROM THE LEFT SET OF NUMBERS FIRST. (Eg: 23=J)

	1	2	3	4	5	6	7
1	A	B	C	D	E	F	G
2	H	I	J	K	L	M	N
3	O	P	Q	R	S	T	U
4	V	W	X	Y	Z		

" S   O   G   O   D
  35 31 17 31 14

C   R   E   A   T   E   D   M   A   N
13 34 15 11 36 15 14 26 11 27

I   N   H   I   S   O   W   N
22 27 21 22 35 31 42 27

I   M   A   G   E ,   I   N   T   H   E
22 26 11 17 15   22 27 36 21 15

I   M   A   G   E   O   F   G   O   D
22 26 11 17 15 31 16 17 31 14

H   E   C   R   E   A   T   E   D
21 15 13 34 15 11 36 15 14

H   I   M ."
21 22 26

GENESIS 1:27

12

•DOT 2 DOT•

CONNECT THE DOTS

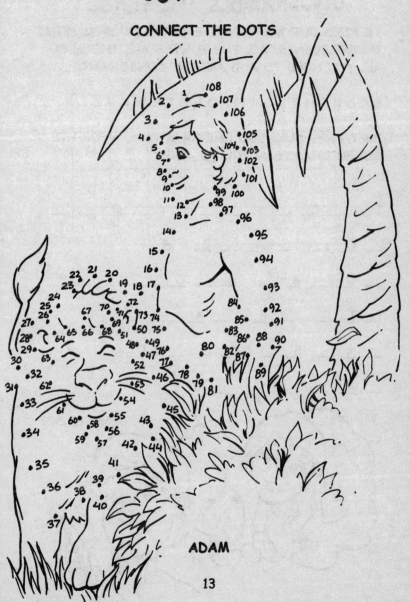

ADAM

13

UNSCRAMBLE THE VERSE

TO FIND OUT WHAT THE VERSE BELOW SAYS, FILL IN THE BLANKS. ALL THE VOWELS ARE THERE, SO ALL YOU NEED TO ADD ARE THE CONSONANTS.

B C D F G H J K L M N P Q R S T V W X Y Z

"NETH HET DLRO DGO DMEA A MWNAO MFOR HTE BIR EH DHA KTEAN TOU FO ANM."

"_ _ E _   _ _ E   _ O _ _
_ O _   _ A _ E _ A _
_ O _ A _   _ _ O _   _ _ E
_ I _   _ E   _ A _
_ A _ E _   O U _   O _
_ A _."

GENESIS 2:22

FINISH THE PICTURE

THIS PICTURE LOOKS A LITTLE UNFINISHED,
DOESN'T IT? A LOT OF THINGS ARE LEFT OUT, SO
WHY DON'T YOU FINISH IT BY FILLING IN AS
MANY MISSING PIECES AS YOU CAN FIND.

15

LOOK-ALIKES

FIND AND CIRCLE SIX DIFFERENCES IN THE
TWO PICTURES BELOW.

16

AMAZING MAZES

AS YOU GO THROUGH THE MAZE, COLLECT THE
LETTERS AND COMPLETE THE STATEMENT BELOW.

GOD IS OUR _ _ _ _ _ _ _ _ _ .

◇ SQUARE GAME ◇

COLOR IN THE AREAS THAT HAVE A SQUARE TO COMPLETE THE VERSE BELOW.

"GOD SAW ALL THAT HE HAD MADE, AND IT WAS VERY __ __ __ __."

GENESIS 1:31

PICTURE FRAMES

WHAT COULD THE PICTURE BE?

DRAW EXACTLY WHAT IS IN EACH NUMBERED
FRAME AT THE TOP OF THE PAGE INTO EACH FRAME
OF THE SAME NUMBER IN THE GRID BELOW.

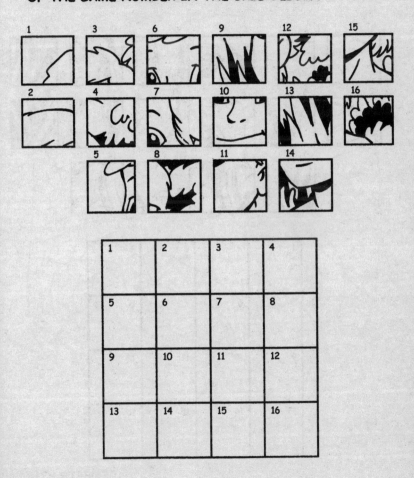

PICTURE FRAMES

WHAT COULD THE PICTURE BE?

DRAW EXACTLY WHAT IS IN EACH NUMBERED
FRAME AT THE TOP OF THE PAGE INTO EACH FRAME
OF THE SAME NUMBER IN THE GRID BELOW.

TRUE / FALSE

1. THE FIRST THING GOD CREATED WAS THE TREES.

TRUE ____ FALSE____

2. GOD SPOKE ALL CREATION INTO EXISTENCE.

TRUE ____ FALSE____

3. MAN CREATED WOMAN.

TRUE ____ FALSE____

4. WE ARE CREATED IN THE IMAGE OF GOD.

TRUE ____ FALSE____

5. GOD NAMED ALL THE ANIMALS.

TRUE ____ FALSE____

WORD SEARCH

CROSS OUT EVERY LETTER THAT APPEARS AT LEAST FOUR TIMES IN THE PUZZLE TO FIND THE WORD THAT COMPLETES THE SENTENCE.

```
B F S J N D L S
Q X C W A G X Q
V N L D J S C V
Q G X B S T V G
C J W V N Q B V
B L H G C E D J
W N D X R C L W
```

GOD THE _ _ _ _ _ _ .

UNSCRAMBLE THE VERSE

TO FIND OUT WHAT THE VERSE BELOW SAYS, FILL IN THE BLANKS. ALL THE VOWELS ARE THERE, SO ALL YOU NEED TO ADD ARE THE CONSONANTS.

B C D F G H J K L M N P Q R S T V W X Z

"A RHTFAE OT HTE HREFATSELS, A FRDDENEE FO DWSOIW, SI DGO NI SIH YHLO WGNDILEL."

"A __A__ __E__ __O __ __E

__A__ __E__ __E__ __, A

__E__E__ __E__ O__ __I__O__ __,

I__ __O__ I__ __I__ __O__Y

__ __E__ __I__ __."

PSALM 68:5

23

CODE BUSTER

USE THE CODE CHART BELOW TO COMPLETE THE VERSE. CHOOSE FROM THE LEFT SET OF NUMBERS FIRST. (Eg: 23=J)

	1	2	3	4	5	6	7
1	A	B	C	D	E	F	G
2	H	I	J	K	L	M	N
3	O	P	Q	R	S	T	U
4	V	W	X	Y	Z		

"

___ ___   ___ ___ ___ ___   ___ ___ ___ ___   ___ ___ ___
21 15   42 22 25 25   13 11 25 25   31 37 36

___ ___   ___ ___ '   ___ ___ ___   ___ ___ ___   ___ ___
36 31   26 15   44 31 37   11 34 15   26 44

___ ___ ___ ___ ___ ___ '   ___ ___   ___ ___ ___'
16 11 36 21 15 34   26 44   17 31 14

___ ___ ___   ___ ___ ___ ___ '   ___ ___
36 21 15   34 31 13 24   26 44

___ ___ ___ ___ ___ ___ ___ . "
35 11 41 22 31 37 34

PSALM 89:26

24

AMAZING MAZES

ADAM AND EVE ARE PLAYING HIDE AND SEEK. BUT THE GARDEN IS SO BIG, THAT ADAM IS HAVING A HARD TIME FINDING EVE. CAN YOU HELP HIM FIND THE WAY?

TWICE THE FUN

UNSCRAMBLE THE UNDERLINED WORDS IN THE VERSE. THEN, ON THE OPPOSITE PAGE, FIND AND CIRCLE THEM IN THE WORD SEARCH PUZZLE.

"BUT YOU ARE OUR <u>HFARET</u>, THOUGH ABRAHAM DOES NOT <u>ONWK</u> US OR <u>SLIEAR</u> ACKNOWLEDGE US; YOU O <u>RLDO</u>, ARE <u>URO</u> FATHER, OUR <u>DMEREERE</u>."

_ _ _ _ _ _   _ _ _ _

_ _ _ _ _ _   _ _ _ _   ISAIAH 63:16

_ _ _   _ _ _ _ _ _ _ _

CONT'D ON THE NEXT PAGE...

```
R G A N L S W K
E Y Q H J O U R
D L D V N F R Z
E W T K A A K D
E J C L Y T X U
M Q Z I B H O F
E I S R A E L E
R W D Y Z R P J
```

ZANY CODE BUSTER

TO DECODE THIS MYSTERY VERSE, LOOK AT EACH LETTER AND WRITE THE ONE THAT COMES <u>BEFORE</u> IT IN THE ALPHABET.

A B C D E F G H I J K L M N O P Q R
S T U V W X Y Z

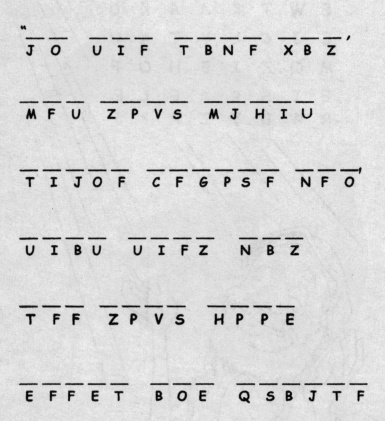

"__ __   __ __ __   __ __ __ __   __ __ __,"
  J O   U I F   T B N F   X B Z

__ __ __   __ __ __ __   __ __ __ __ __
M F U   Z P V S   M J H I U

__ __ __ __ __   __ __ __ __ __ __   __ __ __,'
T I J O F   C F G P S F   N F O

__ __ __ __   __ __ __ __   __ __ __
U I B U   U I F Z   N B Z

__ __ __   __ __ __ __   __ __ __ __
T F F   Z P V S   H P P E

__ __ __ __ __   __ __ __   __ __ __ __ __ __
E F F E T   B O E   Q S B J T F

CONT'D ON THE NEXT PAGE...

Z P V S   G B U I F S   J O

I F B W F O ."

MATTHEW 5:16

NO!
NOT THAT
KIND OF LIGHT!

COLOR THE COMIC

CONT'D ON THE NEXT PAGE...

ZANY CODE BUSTER

USE THE CODE CHART BELOW TO DECODE THE MYSTERY VERSE.

CONT'D ON THE NEXT PAGE...

CONT'D FROM THE PREVIOUS PAGE.

33

WORD SEARCH

FIND AND CIRCLE THE WORDS BELOW IN THE
WORD SEARCH PUZZLE. LOOK UP, DOWN, FORWARD
AND DIAGONALLY TO SOLVE THIS ONE!

```
V K R G S Z I M E Q W O S A
J H D M E U X N C D M R L Q
H D F A T H E R B W G P G D
Y T Y Q M V H T D Z Y K O P
J K N P A E D E W T F S D M
T Q M E A F R J R H W T B L
E S H J D A W E H D Q K C X
R E P T C Q T K R P B C R T
K F T R Z H K S K X S Q N L
P G L I G Y I Z P B O F C N
L O J U R L P L X G N D K B
W K A W Y P W H D P W L E P
S D S Q I V Q M F R D V Q T
G W F P B F X R Q Z O C H R
L Q W L D D Z S H L J W M U
```

FATHER   HEAVEN
SON   GOD
DAUGHTER   LOVE
CHILD   CARE

FINISH THE VERSE

TO FIND OUT WHAT THE VERSE BELOW SAYS, FILL IN THE BLANKS. ALL THE CONSONANTS ARE THERE, SO ALL YOU NEED TO DO IS ADD THE VOWELS.

VOWELS: A E I O U

"_ W_LL B_ _ F_TH_R T_ Y___ _ND Y___ W_LL B_ MY S_NS _ND D___GHT_RS."

2 CORINTHIANS 6:18

35

UNSCRAMBLE AND ANSWER

FIRST, UNSCRAMBLE THE WORDS AND WRITE THEM
IN THE SPACE BELOW. THEN, ON THE FOLLOWING
PAGE, LIST ALL THE CIRCLED LETTERS AND
UNSCRAMBLE THEM TO SPELL OUT THE ANSWER TO
THE QUESTION.

"ON EON SHA ENSE HTE HTRAFE

___ ___ O___ ___ ___ O___

CTEPXE HET EON HWO SI RMFO

___ ___ ___ ___ ___ O___

DGO; NYOL EH SHA ENSE HTE

___ ___ __O___ ___ O___

EAHFRT."

___ O___

JOHN 6:46

CONT'D ON THE NEXT PAGE...

36

CONT'D FROM THE PREVIOUS PAGE.

◯ ◯ ◯ ◯ ◯ ◯
‾ ‾ ‾ ‾ ‾ ‾

GOD IS OUR HEAVENLY _ _ _ _ _ _ _ !

FINISH THE VERSE

TO FIND OUT WHAT THE VERSE BELOW SAYS, FILL
IN THE BLANKS. ALL THE CONSONANTS ARE THERE,
SO ALL YOU NEED TO DO IS ADD THE VOWELS.

VOWELS: A E I O U

"MY F__TH__R, WH__ H__S

G__V__N TH__M T__ M__ __S

GR____T__R TH__N __LL; N__

__N__ C__N SN__TCH TH__M

____T __F MY F__TH__R'S

H__ND. __ __ND TH__ F__TH__R

__R__ __N__."

JOHN 10:29-30

HIDDEN ALPHABET

FIND AND CIRCLE EVERY LETTER OF THE ALPHABET
THAT HAS BEEN HIDDEN IN THIS PICTURE.

39

FINISH THE PICTURE

USING THE GRID, DRAW THE PICTURE BELOW ON THE FOLLOWING PAGE.

IN THE FATHER'S HAND!

FROM THE PREVIOUS PAGE, USE THE GRID TO
DRAW THE PICTURE FOR YOURSELF.

CODE BUSTER

USE THE CODE CHART BELOW TO COMPLETE THE VERSE. CHOOSE FROM THE LEFT SET OF NUMBERS FIRST. (Eg: 23=J)

	1	2	3	4	5	6	7
1	A	B	C	D	E	F	G
2	H	I	J	K	L	M	N
3	O	P	Q	R	S	T	U
4	V	W	X	Y	Z		

"___ ___ ___ ___ ___   ___ ___ ___ ___   ___ ___'
 23 15 35 37 35   35 11 22 14   14 31

___ ___ ___   ___ ___ ___ ___   ___ ___   ___ ___
27 31 36   21 31 25 14   31 27   36 31

___ ___   ___ ___ ___   ___   ___ ___ ___ ___
26 15   16 31 34   22   21 11 41 15

___ ___ ___   ___ ___ ___   ___ ___ ___ ___ ___ ___ ___ ___
27 31 36   44 15 36   34 15 36 37 34 27 15 14

___ ___   ___ ___ ___   ___ ___ ___ ___ ___ ___ .
36 31   36 21 15   16 11 36 21 15 34

CONT'D ON THE NEXT PAGE...

__ __   __ __ __ __ __ __ __   __ __   __ __
17 31   22 27 35 36 15 11 14   36 31   26 44

__ __ __ __ __ __ __ __   __ __ __
12 34 31 36 21 15 34 35   11 27 14

__ __ __ __   __ __ __ __ ,   " __   __ __
36 15 25 25   36 21 15 26   22   11 26

__ __ __ __ __ __ __ __ __   __ __   __ __
34 15 36 37 34 27 22 27 17   36 31   26 44

__ __ __ __ __ __   __ __ __   __ __ __ __
16 11 36 21 15 34   11 27 14   44 31 37 34

__ __ __ __ __ __ ,   __ __   __ __   __ __ __
16 11 36 21 15 34   36 31   26 44   17 31 14

__ __ __   __ __ __ __   __ __ __ . " "
11 27 14   44 31 37 34   17 31 14

JOHN 20:17

43

WORD SEARCH

HOW MANY TIMES CAN YOU FIND THE WORD
<u>FATHER</u> IN THE WORD SEARCH PUZZLE BELOW.
LOOK UP, DOWN, FORWARD AND DIAGONALLY TO
SOLVE THIS ONE!

```
R S K L Y B D T S F J F K Z
P F D J Z F G T X Y L A V T
X G A F S P R K D J B T Z S
K J L T D E Y F Z G V H X P
F T D X H P G J S L B E Z F
S Z V T F E L T D Y X R G J
B G A D B J R F Z F P B T V
L F Y X F Z G P V A L J D B
D Z S J L B K F Y T X S L K
T K P F D T F A T H E R X D
P L B Y J K Z D X E K B L F
F K F A T H E R Y R Y D T J
```

44

SQUARE GAME

COLOR IN THE AREAS THAT HAVE A SQUARE TO COMPLETE THE SENTENCE BELOW.

GOD IS <u>MY</u> _ _ _ _ _ _ _ !

COLOR THE PICTURE

GOD THE SON

FILL IN THE BLANKS

"AND A _ _ _ _ _ _ FROM _ _ _ _ _ _ _

SAID, '_ _ _ _ IS MY _ _ _ _, WHOM I

_ _ _ _ _; WITH _ _ _ _ I _ _ WELL

_ _ _ _ _ _ _ _ .'"

MATTHEW 3:17

47

FINISH THE VERSE

TO FIND OUT WHAT THE VERSE BELOW SAYS, FILL
IN THE BLANKS. ALL THE CONSONANTS ARE THERE
SO ALL YOU NEED TO DO IS ADD THE VOWELS.

VOWELS: A E I O U

"_ _LL TH_ _NGS H_ V_ B_ _ _N

C_ _MM_ _TT_ _D T_ M_ BY MY

F_ _TH_ _R. N_ _ _N_ KN_ _WS

TH_ _ S_ _N _ _XC_ _PT TH_ _

F_ _TH_ _R, _ _ND N_ _ _N_

KN_ _WS TH_ _ F_ _TH_ _R

CONT'D ON THE NEXT PAGE...

48

CONT'D FROM THE PREVIOUS PAGE

__XC__PT TH__ S__N __ND

TH__S__ T__ WH__M TH__

S__N CH___S__ST__

R__V___L H__M."

MATTHEW 11:27

49

ZANY CODE BUSTER

TO DECODE THIS MYSTERY VERSE, LOOK AT EACH LETTER AND WRITE THE ONE THAT COMES <u>BEFORE</u> IT IN THE ALPHABET.

A B C D E F G H I J K L M N O P Q R
S T U V W X Y Z

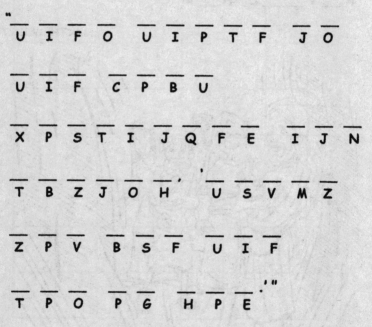

"<u>T</u> <u>H</u> <u>E</u>   <u>T</u> <u>H</u> <u>O</u> <u>S</u> <u>E</u>   <u>I</u> <u>N</u>
 U I F   U I P T F   J O

<u>T</u> <u>H</u> <u>E</u>   <u>B</u> <u>O</u> <u>A</u> <u>T</u>
 U I F   C P B U

<u>W</u> <u>O</u> <u>R</u> <u>S</u> <u>H</u> <u>I</u> <u>P</u> <u>E</u> <u>D</u>   <u>H</u> <u>I</u> <u>M</u>
 X P S T I J Q F E   I J N

<u>S</u> <u>A</u> <u>Y</u> <u>I</u> <u>N</u> <u>G</u> , '<u>T</u> <u>R</u> <u>U</u> <u>L</u> <u>Y</u>
 T B Z J O H   U S V M Z

<u>Y</u> <u>O</u> <u>U</u>   <u>A</u> <u>R</u> <u>E</u>   <u>T</u> <u>H</u> <u>E</u>
 Z P V   B S F   U I F

<u>S</u> <u>O</u> <u>N</u>   <u>O</u> <u>F</u>   <u>G</u> <u>O</u> <u>D</u> .'"
 T P O   P G   H P E

MATTHEW 14:33

FINISH THE PICTURE

USING THE GRID, COMPLETE THE PICTURE BY DUPLICATING THE FINISHED HALF ONTO THE UNFINISHED AREA. TWO SQUARES HAVE ALREADY BEEN STARTED FOR YOU.

JESUS, THE SON OF GOD

TWICE THE FUN

UNSCRAMBLE THE UNDERLINED WORDS IN EACH VERSE. THEN, ON THE OPPOSITE PAGE, FIND AND CIRCLE THEM IN THE WORD SEARCH PUZZLE.

1. "SIMON PETER ANSWERED, ' YOU ARE THE <u>RSITHC</u>, THE <u>NSO</u> OF THE LIVING <u>OGD</u>.'"

MATTHEW 16:16

— — — — — —   — — —   — — —

2. "A <u>COVEI</u> CAME FROM THE <u>UCDOL</u>, SAYING, 'THIS IS MY SON WHOM I HAVE CHOSEN; <u>ETLISN</u> TO <u>IMH</u>.'"

LUKE 9:35

— — — — — —   — — — — — —

— — — — — — —   — — —

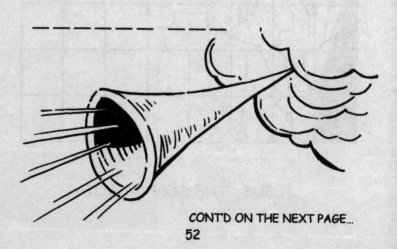

CONT'D ON THE NEXT PAGE...

```
J  R  E  V  P  S  Z  Q  K
L  C  L  O  U  D  F  M  T
N  B  C  I  W  L  Q  B  W
H  N  J  C  H  R  I  S  T
H  Y  H  E  B  G  G  O  D
L  I  S  T  E  N  K  N  Z
M  J  M  W  D  Q  R  S  J
```

WORD JUMBLE

FILL IN THE BLANK SPACES BY WRITING IN THE
OPPOSITE OF EACH WORD BELOW, ANSWERING
EACH CLUE CORRECTLY. USING THE LETTERS IN THE
CIRCLES, COMPLETE THE SENTENCE BELOW.

MOTHER   _ _ _ _ _ _

DAUGHTER   _ ◯ _

DARK   _ _ _ _ _

END   _ ◯ _ _ _ _ _ _

NIGHT   ◯ _ _

MAN   _ _ _ _ _

THE FATHER AND THE SON ARE BOTH :

◯ ◯ ◯

54

WORD SEARCH

HOW MANY TIMES CAN YOU FIND THE WORD, <u>SON</u>
BELOW IN THE WORD SEARCH PUZZLE? LOOK UP,
DOWN, FORWARD AND DIAGONALLY TO SOLVE
THIS ONE!

```
B K H Z P T F S C J R Z H N
T S R J Z X N W B M K P O Z
Z F O C H S P R Z T J S F C
P S T N B K F C Q H X Z R P
C R J Z P S X T M S B F E K
S T H F K R C Z J O P X S T
O B Z S T X Q F N C K H J
N J F R M C Z S P J X F T Z
T K S O N H B W R Z M C P S
C J P R T N S N K F J S R B
Z B F K O C P Z T S C O H X
P H T S C R F B S J K N B Z
```

55

UNSCRAMBLE AND ANSWER

FIRST, UNSCRAMBLE THE WORDS AND WRITE THEM IN THE SPACES UNDER EACH WORD. THEN LIST ALL THE CIRCLED LETTERS BELOW AND UNSCRAMBLE THEM TO SPELL OUT THE ANSWER TO THE QUESTION.

"OFR   DGO   OS   VEOLD   ETH

____ (__) (__) ____ ____

LRWDO   AHTT   EH   EGVA   IHS

(__)____ ____ __ ____ ___

NEO   DAN   LOYN   NSO."

(__)____ ____ (__)____ (__)____

JOHN 3:16

WHO IS JESUS CHRIST?

(__)(__)(__)'(__) (__)(__)(__)!

56

AMAZING MAZES

AS YOU GO THROUGH THE MAZE, COLLECT THE LETTERS AND COMPLETE THE STATEMENT BELOW.

GOD _ _ _ _ _ _ _ ME.

FINISH THE VERSE

TO FIND OUT WHAT THE VERSE BELOW SAYS, FILL IN THE BLANKS. ALL THE CONSONANTS ARE THERE, SO ALL YOU NEED TO DO IS ADD THE VOWELS.

VOWELS: A E I O U

"F _ TH _ R, TH _ T _ M _ H _ S

C _ ME. GL _ R _ FY Y _ _ _ R

S _ N, TH _ T Y _ _ R S _ N

M _ Y GL _ R _ FY Y _ _ _ ."

JOHN 17:1

58

WORD SEARCH

FIND AND CIRCLE THE WORDS BELOW IN THE
WORD SEARCH PUZZLE. LOOK UP, DOWN, FORWARD
AND DIAGONALLY TO SOLVE THIS ONE!

```
R D B K V T J S Z C F G L X
V J S C H R I S T D R B K T
T Z C X D B K F I V G J S C
F G K J R T V S M B Z X D L
S B J C Z X L J E F T K R E
D T E V K B S C Z G X S V J
J R S X C D O V K B F O Z T
B V U K T S N X J R L D G C
C Z S D J B C F T V S L K X
S G X K R T Z D L C J W B Q
V B D F A T H E R K T S Z R
J Z L T R K V B S J X D G C
G C X S Z D J T G C L V K B
O T K V B R G L O R I F Y D
D S C D X J Z K V T B R S J
```

CHRIST   TIME
GOD   GLORIFY
JESUS   SON
LOVE   FATHER

59

CODE BUSTER

USE THE CODE CHART BELOW TO COMPLETE THE VERSE. CHOOSE FROM THE LEFT SET OF NUMBERS FIRST. (Eg: 23=J)

	1	2	3	4	5	6	7
1	A	B	C	D	E	F	G
2	H	I	J	K	L	M	N
3	O	P	Q	R	S	T	U
4	V	W	X	Y	Z		

"

___ ___ ___   ___ ___ ___   ___ ___ ___ ___ ___ ___ ___
11 27 14   42 21 31   36 21 34 31 37 17 21

___ ___ ___   ___   ___ ___ ___ ___ ___   ___ ___
36 21 15   35   32 22 34 22 36   31 16

___ ___ ___ ___ ___ ___ ___ ___   ___ ___ ___
21 31 25 22 27 15 35 35   42 11 35

___ ___ ___ ___ ___ ___ ___ ___   ___ ___ ___ ___
14 15 13 25 11 34 15 14   42 22 36 21

___ ___ ___ ___ ___   ___ ___   ___ ___   ___ ___ ___
32 31 42 15 34   36 31   12 15   36 21 15

___ ___ ___   ___ ___   ___ ___ ___
35 31 27   31 16   17 31 14

CONT'D ON THE NEXT PAGE...

60

CONT'D FROM THE PREVIOUS PAGE

___ ___   ___ ___ ___   ___ ___ ___ ___ ___ ___ ___ ___ -
12 44   21 22 35   34 15 35 37 34 34 15 13

___ ___ ___ ___   ___ ___ ___ ___   ___ ___ ___
36 22 31 27   16 34 31 26   36 21 15

___ ___ ___ ___ : ___ ___ ___ ___ ___   ___ ___ ___ ___ ___ ___
14 15 11 14   23 15 35 37 35   13 21 34 22 35 36

___ ___ ___   ___ ___ ___ ___ . "
31 37 34   25 31 34 14

ROMANS 1:4

61

ZANY CODE BUSTER

USE THE CODE CHART BELOW TO DECODE THE MYSTERY VERSE.

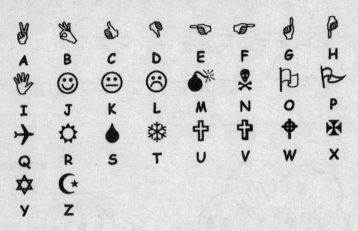

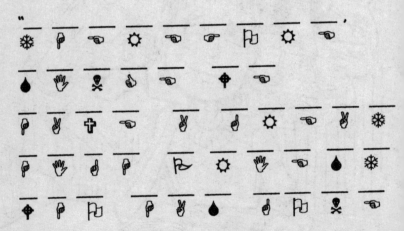

CONT'D ON THE NEXT PAGE...

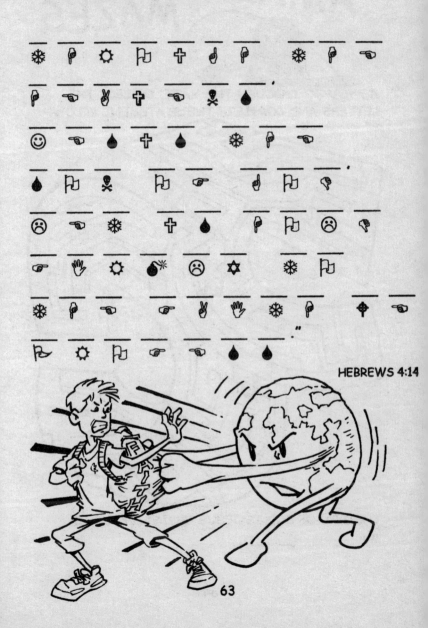

HEBREWS 4:14

AMAZING MAZES

AS YOU GO THROUGH THE MAZE, COLLECT THE LETTERS AND COMPLETE THE STATEMENT BELOW.

THE SON OF GOD IS JESUS CHRIST...JESUS IS MY __ __ __ __ .

ZANY CODE BUSTER

TO DECODE THIS MYSTERY VERSE, LOOK AT EACH
LETTER AND WRITE THE ONE THAT COMES <u>BEFORE</u>
IT IN THE ALPHABET.

A B C D E F G H I J K L M N O P Q R
S T U V W X Y Z

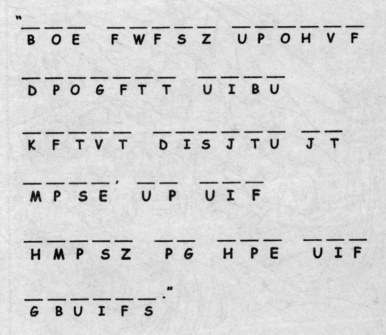

"___ ___ _____ _____

B O E   F W F S Z   U P O H V F

_____ ____

D P O G F T T   U I B U

____ _____ __

K F T V T   D I S J T U   J T

____' __ ___

M P S E   U P   U I F

_____ __ ____ ____

H M P S Z   P G   H P E   U I F

_____."

G B U I F S

PHILIPPIANS 2:11

FINISH THE PICTURE

THIS PICTURE LOOKS A LITTLE UNFINISHED, DOESN'T IT? A LOT OF THINGS ARE LEFT OUT, SO WHY DON'T YOU FINISH IT BY FILLING IN AS MANY MISSING PIECES AS YOU CAN FIND.

UNSCRAMBLE THE VERSE

TO FIND OUT WHAT THE VERSE BELOW SAYS, FILL
IN THE BLANKS. ALL THE VOWELS ARE THERE, SO ALL
YOU NEED TO ADD ARE THE CONSONANTS.

" OS EHNT, UTJS SA OYU ICEDVREE SEJUS TRHICS
SA RLDO TUCNOINE OT ELVI NI IHM."

"_O __E__, _U__ A_ _OU

_E_EI_E_ _E_U_ ____I__

A_ _O__, _O__I_UE _O

_I_E I_ _I_."

COLOSSIANS 2:6

I
THINK
THERE'S
MORE TO IT
THAN THAT!

LOOK-ALIKES

FIND AND CIRCLE EIGHT DIFFERENCES IN THE TWO PICTURES BELOW.

PICTURE FRAMES
WHAT COULD THE PICTURE BE?

DRAW EXACTLY WHAT IS IN EACH NUMBERED
FRAME AT THE TOP OF THE PAGE INTO EACH FRAME
OF THE SAME NUMBER IN THE GRID BELOW.

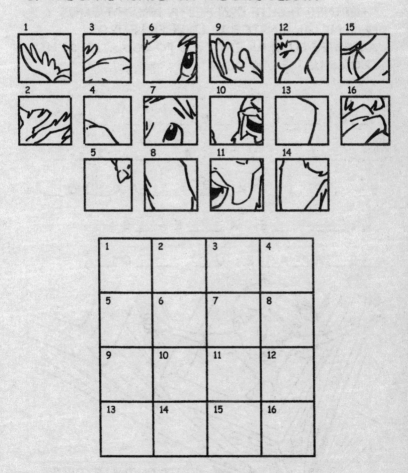

UNSCRAMBLE THE VERSE

TO FIND OUT WHAT THE VERSE BELOW SAYS, FILL IN THE BLANKS. ALL THE VOWELS ARE THERE, SO ALL YOU NEED TO ADD ARE THE CONSONANTS.

" HERINET IHGHTE ORN HEDTP, NRO HYNGANIT SELE NI LAL ANRTOECI, LWLI EB LEAB OT AARESTPE SU OFMR EHT EVLO FO OGD ATHT SI NI IRTHCS USJSE URO DOLR."

"__ E I __ __ E __   __ E I __ __ __   __ O __

__ E __ __ __ __ ,   __ O __   A __ Y __ __ I __ __

E __ __ E I __   A __ __   __ __ E A __ I O __ ,

__ I __ __   __ E A __ __ E   __ O

__ E __ A __ A __ E U __   __ __ O __

CONT'D ON THE NEXT PAGE...

CONT'D FROM THE PREVIOUS PAGE.

__E _O_E O_ _O_

__A_ I_ I_ ___I__

_E_U_ OU_ _O__."

ROMANS 8:39

WORD SEARCH

CROSS OUT EVERY LETTER THAT APPEARS FOUR TIMES IN THE PUZZLE TO FIND THE WORD THAT COMPLETES THE SENTENCE.

```
H V B J S G Z N
D T Z X P C B T
T P S F I K F K
G J N Z G I J O
H C X X H F I V
N B L V K T C R
Z G I P J S N B
S X K C F V P H
```

JESUS IS _ _ _ _ OF ALL !

HIDDEN ALPHABET

FIND AND CIRCLE EVERY LETTER OF THE ALPHABET
THAT HAS BEEN HIDDEN IN THIS PICTURE.

73

CODE BUSTER

USE THE CODE CHART BELOW TO COMPLETE THE VERSE. CHOOSE FROM THE LEFT SET OF NUMBERS FIRST. (Eg: 23=J)

	1	2	3	4	5	6	7
1	A	B	C	D	E	F	G
2	H	I	J	K	L	M	N
3	O	P	Q	R	S	T	U
4	V	W	X	Y	Z		

" A N D   W E   H A V E   S E E N
11 27 14   42 15   21 11 41 15   35 15 15 27

A N D   T E S T I F Y   T H A T
11 27 14   36 15 35 36 22 16 44   36 21 11 36

T H E   F A T H E R   H A S
36 21 15   16 11 36 21 15 34   21 11 35

S E N T   H I S   S O N   T O
35 15 27 36   21 22 35   35 31 27   36 31

B E   S A V I O U R   O F
12 15   35 11 41 22 31 37 34   31 16

T H E   W O R L D ."
36 21 15   42 31 34 25 14

1 JOHN 4:14

74

UNSCRAMBLE THE VERSE

TO FIND OUT WHAT THE VERSE BELOW SAYS, FILL
IN THE BLANKS. ALL THE VOWELS ARE THERE, SO ALL
YOU NEED TO ADD ARE THE CONSONANTS.

" OYU EAR LAL OSSN FO DGO GRUTHOH IFAHT NI
CSITRH SSEJU, OFR LAL FO UYO HOW EEWR
TBDEAPIZ TINO IRTHCS AEVH EDCOLHT
SSVEUERYOL HWTI RSICTH."

" _ OU   A _ E   A _ _   _ O _ _   O _

_ O _   _ _ _ OU _ _   _ A I _ _ _

I _   _ _ _ I _ _   _ E _ U _, _ O _

A _ _   O _   _ OU   _ _ O   _ E _ E

_ A _ _ I _ E _   I _ _ O   _ _ _ I _ _

_ A _ E   _ _ O _ _ E _   _ OU _ -

_ E _ _ E _   _ I _ _   _ _ _ I _ _ ."

GALATIANS 3:26-27

75

COLOR THE COMIC

CONT'D ON THE NEXT PAGE...

HIDDEN ALPHABET

FIND AND CIRCLE EVERY LETTER OF THE ALPHABET THAT HAS BEEN HIDDEN IN THIS PICTURE. THEN, USING THOSE LETTERS, COMPLETE THE STATEMENT BELOW.

I AM GOD'S __ __ __ __ __ !

COLOR THE PICTURE

THE HOLY SPIRIT IS GOD

FINISH THE VERSE

TO FIND OUT WHAT THE VERSE BELOW SAYS, FILL IN THE BLANKS. ALL THE CONSONANTS ARE THERE, SO ALL YOU NEED TO DO IS ADD THE VOWELS.

VOWELS: A E I O U

"N __ W TH __ __ __ RTH W __ S

F __ RML __ SS __ ND __ MPTY

D __ RKN __ SS W __ S __ V __ R

TH __ S __ RF __ C __ __ F TH __

D __ __ P __ ND TH __ SP __ R __ T

__ F G __ D W __ S H __ V __ R __ NG

__ V __ R TH __ W __ T __ RS."

GENESIS 1:2

80

TWICE THE FUN

UNSCRAMBLE THE UNDERLINED WORDS IN EACH VERSE. THEN, ON THE NEXT PAGE, FIND AND CIRCLE THEM IN THE WORD SEARCH PUZZLE.

1. "WHERE CAN I GO FROM YOUR <u>TSIPIR</u>?"
"WHERE CAN I FLEE FROM YOUR <u>EPRCENES</u>?"

_ _ _ _ _ _   _ _ _ _ _ _ _ _

PSALM 139:7

2. "I WILL <u>RPUO</u> OUT MY SPIRIT ON YOUR <u>GONFIFRSPR</u>."

_ _ _ _   _ _ _ _ _ _ _ _ _

ISAIAH 44:3

3. "AND I HAVE <u>DFEILL</u> HIM WITH THE SPIRIT OF <u>OGD</u>."

_ _ _ _ _ _   _ _ _

EXODUS 31:3

CONT'D ON THE NEXT PAGE...

CONT'D FROM THE PREVIOUS PAGE.

```
D G P P F G H B O
S P I R I T V Y F
P L B E L U T Z F
O K D S L R N D S
U G H E E P V G P
R D K N D O G U R
H S Y C F O C R I
O S P E D K Y P N
D G H E Y C J J G
```

CODE BUSTER

USE THE CODE CHART BELOW TO COMPLETE THE VERSE. CHOOSE FROM THE LEFT SET OF NUMBERS FIRST. (Eg: 23=J)

	1	2	3	4	5	6	7
1	A	B	C	D	E	F	G
2	H	I	J	K	L	M	N
3	O	P	Q	R	S	T	U
4	V	W	X	Y	Z		

" __ __ __ __ __ __ __ __   __ __ __
  22 12 11 32 36 22 45 15   44 31 37

__ __ __ __   __ __ __ __ __   __ __ __
42 22 36 21   42 11 36 15 34   16 31 34

__ __ __ __ __ __ __ __ __ __'   __ __ __
34 15 32 15 27 36 11 27 13 15   12 37 36

__ __ __ __ __   __ __   __ __ __ __
11 16 36 15 34   26 15   42 22 25 25

__ __ __ __   __ __ __   __ __ __   __ __
13 31 26 15   31 27 15   42 21 31   22 35

CONT'D ON THE NEXT PAGE...

83

——— ——— ——— ——— ——— ——— ——— ——— ——— ——— ——— ———
26 31 34 15 32 31 42 15 34 16 37 25

——— ——— ——— ——— ——— ' ——— ——— ——— ——— ———
36 21 11 27 22   42 21 31 35 15

——— ——— ——— ——— ——— ——— ——— ——— ——— ——— ——— ——— ———
35 11 27 14 11 25 35 22 11 26 27 31 36

——— ——— ——— ——— ——— ——— ——— ——— ——— . ——— ———
16 22 36 36 31 13 11 34 34 44 21 15

——— ——— ——— ——— ——— ——— ——— ——— ——— ——— ——— ——— ——— ———
42 22 25 25 12 11 32 36 22 45 15 44 31 37

——— ——— ——— ——— ——— ——— ——— ——— ——— ——— ———
42 22 36 21 36 21 15 21 31 25 44

——— ——— ——— ——— ——— ——— ——— ——— ——— ——— ——— ——— ——— "
35 32 22 34 22 36 11 27 14 16 22 34 15

MATTHEW 3:11

UNSCRAMBLE THE VERSE

TO FIND OUT WHAT THE VERSE BELOW SAYS, FILL IN THE BLANKS. ALL THE VOWELS ARE THERE, SO ALL YOU NEED TO ADD ARE THE CONSONANTS.

"FI UYO NTEH, HTGHUO UYO EAR LEIV, WKON WHO OT EGVI OOGD FGTSI OT RYUO NCHEIRDL, WHO UMHC EMRO LWIL RYUO RTAHFE NI NHEEAV EGVI HET YHOL TIIRPS OT ETSHO OWH KAS MHI!"

"I__ __OU __ __EN, __ __ OU__ __

__OU A__E E__I__, __ __ O__

__O__ __O __I__E __OO__

__I__ __ __ __O __OU__

__ __I__ __ __E__, __O__ __U__ __

__O__E __I__ __ __OU__

__A__ __E__ I__ __EA__E__

__I__E __ __E __O__ __ __ __I__I__

__O __ __O__E __ __O A__ __ __I__!"

AMAZING MAZES

THE HOLY SPIRIT WANTS TO COME TO YOU. GO
THROUGH THE MAZE TO FIND THE PATH HE TAKES.

FILL IN THE BLANKS

WORD LIST:

COUNSELOR   REMIND
EVERYTHING   HOLY SPIRIT
NAME   FATHER
TEACH   THINGS

"BUT THE _ _ _ _ _ _ _ _ _, THE

_ _ _ _ _ _ _ _ _ _, WHOM THE

_ _ _ _ _ _ WILL SEND IN MY

_ _ _ _, WILL _ _ _ _ _ YOU ALL

_ _ _ _ _ _ AND WILL _ _ _ _ _ _

YOU OF _ _ _ _ _ _ _ _ _ _ I HAVE

SAID TO YOU."

JOHN 14:26

SQUARE GAME

COLOR IN THE AREAS THAT HAVE A SQUARE TO
FIND THE ANSWER TO COMPLETE THE VERSE BELOW.

"BUT WHEN HE, THE _ _ _ _ _ _ _ OF
TRUTH, COMES, HE WILL GUIDE YOU INTO ALL
TRUTH."

JOHN 16:13

LOOK-ALIKES

FIND AND CIRCLE TEN DIFFERENCES IN THE
TWO PICTURES BELOW.

ZANY CODE BUSTER

USE THE CODE CHART BELOW TO DECODE THE MYSTERY VERSE.

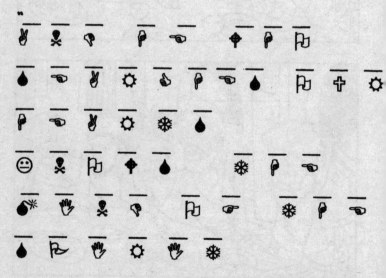

CONT'D ON THE NEXT PAGE...

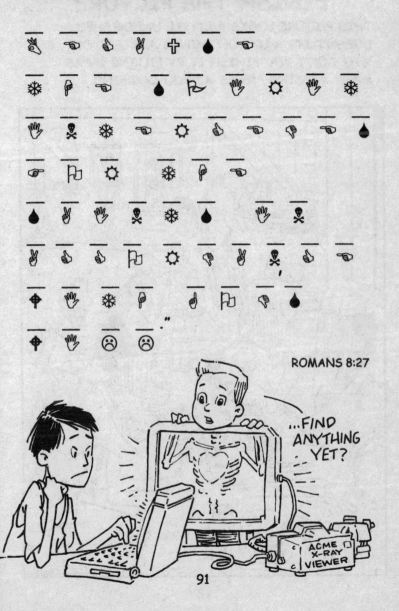

ROMANS 8:27

...FIND ANYTHING YET?

ACME X-RAY VIEWER

91

FINISH THE PICTURE

THIS PICTURE LOOKS A LITTLE UNFINISHED, DOESN'T IT? A LOT OF THINGS ARE LEFT OUT, SO WHY DON'T YOU FINISH IT BY FILLING IN AS MANY MISSING PIECES AS YOU CAN FIND.

AMAZING MAZES

AS YOU GO THROUGH THE MAZE, COLLECT THE LETTERS AND COMPLETE THE VERSE BELOW.

"BUT GOD HAS REVEALED IT TO US BY HIS
_ _ _ _ _ _. THE SPIRIT SEARCHES ALL
THINGS, EVEN THE DEEP THINGS OF GOD."

1 CORINTHIANS 2:10

CODE BUSTER

USE THE CODE CHART BELOW TO COMPLETE THE
VERSE. CHOOSE FROM THE LEFT SET OF NUMBERS
FIRST. (Eg: 23=J)

	1	2	3	4	5	6	7
1	A	B	C	D	E	F	G
2	H	I	J	K	L	M	N
3	O	P	Q	R	S	T	U
4	V	W	X	Y	Z		

"

— —   — — — —   — — —
42 15   21 11 41 15   27 31 36

— — — — — — — —   — — —
34 15 13 15 22 41 15 14   36 21 15

— — — — — —   — —   — — —
35 32 22 34 22 36   31 16   36 21 15

— — — — — —,   — — —   — — —
42 31 34 25 14   12 37 36   36 21 15

— — — — — —   — — —   — —
35 32 22 34 22 36   42 21 31   22 35

CON'T ON THE NEXT PAGE...

___ ___ ___ ___   ___ ___ ___'   ___ ___ ___ ___   ___ ___
16 34 31 26   17 31 14   36 21 11 36   42 15

___ ___ ___   ___ ___ ___ ___ ___ ___ ___ ___ ___
26 11 44   37 27 14 15 34 35 36 11 27 14

___ ___ ___ ___   ___ ___ ___   ___ ___ ___
42 21 11 36   17 31 14   21 11 35

___ ___ ___ ___ ___ ___   ___ ___ ___ ___ ___
16 34 15 15 25 44   17 22 41 15 27

___ ___ ."
37 35

1 CORINTHIANS 2:12

GO AWAY!
I'VE TOLD YOU
BEFORE... I ALREADY
HAVE THE ONLY SPIRIT
I'LL EVER NEED!

FILL IN THE BLANKS

WORD LIST:

RECEIVED	TEMPLE
KNOW	HOLY SPIRIT
YOU	GOD
BODY	YOUR

"DO YOU NOT _ _ _ _ THAT _ _ _ _ _

_ _ _ _ _ IS A _ _ _ _ _ _ OF THE

_ _ _ _ _ _ _ _ _ _ WHO IS IN

_ _ _, WHOM YOU HAVE

_ _ _ _ _ _ _ _ _ _ FROM _ _ _?"

1 CORINTHIANS 6:19

DOES HE SEEM DIFFERENT TO YOU, TODAY?

96

UNSCRAMBLE AND ANSWER

FIRST, UNSCRAMBLE THE WORDS AND WRITE
THEM IN THE SPACES UNDER EACH WORD. THEN
LIST ALL THE CIRCLED LETTERS BELOW AND
UNSCRAMBLE THEM TO ANSWER THE QUESTION.

"EH   DAENTONI   SU,   TSE

◯___   _____   ___   ___

SHI   LSEA   FO   POIWHNSER

___   ____   __   ___◯____

NO   SU   DAN   TPU   SHI   TPSIIR

__   __   ◯___   ___   ___   _____

NI   RUO   SHTERA   SA   A

__   ___   _____   __   _

CONT'D ON THE NEXT PAGE...

TDIESPO,   GGNUIAEREATN

_____ _____⭕_____

TWAH   SI   OT   ECMO."

_____ _ _ _____⭕

2 CORINTHIANS 1:22

WHERE DOES THE HOLY SPIRIT LIVE?

IN MY ⭕⭕⭕⭕⭕.

98

PICTURE FRAMES

WHAT COULD THE PICTURE BE?

DRAW EXACTLY WHAT IS IN EACH NUMBERED
FRAME AT THE TOP OF THE PAGE INTO EACH FRAME
OF THE SAME NUMBER IN THE GRID BELOW.

1	2	3	4
5	6	7	8
9	10	11	12
13	14	15	16

ZANY CODE BUSTER

USE THE CODE CHART BELOW TO DECODE THE MYSTERY VERSE.

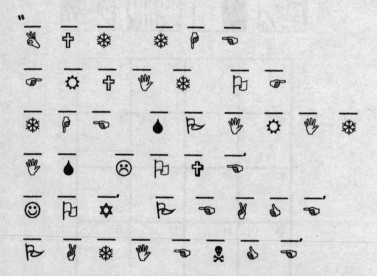

CONT'D ON THE NEXT PAGE...

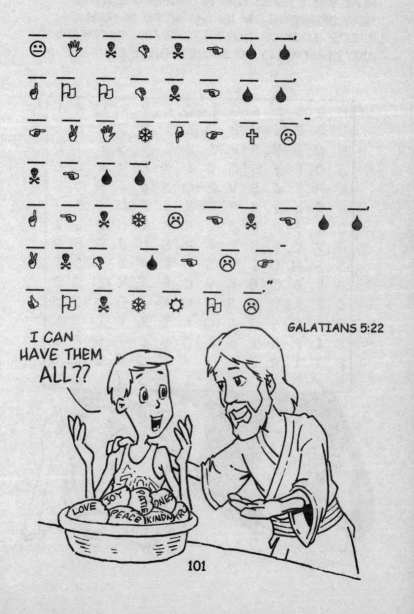

GALATIANS 5:22

WORD SEARCH

HOW MANY TIMES CAN YOU FIND THE WORD
HOLY SPIRIT BELOW IN THE WORD SEARCH
PUZZLE. LOOK UP, DOWN, FORWARD, BACKWARDS
AND DIAGONALLY TO SOLVE THIS ONE!

```
H D S F G J L C K V P Q K I
L O C K V P Q K I D J G F S
H O L Y S P I R I T S F J G
S D F Y G J K I Q P V K C L
L H K C S V P Q S K J G D F
H O L Y S P I R I T D S F T
D L S F G J I K P V K C L I
C Y L K V K P R S D J G F R
S S H O L Y S P I R I T D I
F P G J D K V C P T K L S P
C I K V L S P Q K G F D J S
D R F G J C Q K I P K L S Y
S I P G K K L D V C J G F L
F T I R I P S Y L O H S D O
P X D S T I R I P S Y L O H
```

102

COLOR THE COMIC

CONT'D ON THE NEXT PAGE...

CONT'D ON THE NEXT PAGE...

CONT'D FROM THE PREVIOUS PAGE.

•DOT 2 DOT•

CONNECT THE DOTS

HIDDEN ALPHABET

FIND AND CIRCLE EVERY LETTER OF THE ALPHABET
THAT HAS BEEN HIDDEN IN THIS PICTURE AND
FINISH THE SENTENCE BELOW.

THE HOLY SPIRIT IS MY _ _ _ _ _ _ _.

MULTIPLE CHOICE

CIRCLE THE CORRECT ANSWER.

1. "IN THE BEGINNING GOD CREATED THE...

    A. SEA"
    B. HEAVENS AND EARTH"
    C. APPLE TREE"

2. GOD MADE MAN IN THE IMAGE OF...

    A. MONKEYS
    B MAN
    C. GOD

3. GOD CREATED EVE OUT OF ADAM'S...

    A. RIB
    B. ARM
    C. TOE

CONT'D ON THE NEXT PAGE...

CONT'D FROM THE PREVIOUS PAGE.

4. WE ARE CHILDREN OF...

    A. GOD
    B. ADAM
    C. OUR PARENTS

5. WHEN JESUS CALLED GOD, "ABBA", HE WAS
   SAYING...

    A. FATHER
    B. CREATOR
    C. LORD

6. WE BELIEVE IN...

    A. ONE GOD
    B. THREE GODS
    C. ONE GOD IN THREE PERSONS

TRUE / FALSE

1. A VOICE CAME FROM HEAVEN AND SAID "THIS IS JESUS."

TRUE ___ FALSE___

2. GOD CREATED EVE.

TRUE ___ FALSE___

3. JESUS CHRIST IS THE SON OF GOD.

TRUE ___ FALSE___

4. JESUS USED HIS GODLY POWERS DURING HIS MINISTRY.

TRUE ___ FALSE___

5. JESUS IS SAVIOUR OF THE WORLD.

TRUE ___ FALSE___

TRUE / FALSE

1. WE BECOME CHILDREN OF GOD BY GOING TO CHURCH.

    TRUE ____ FALSE____

2. THE HOLY SPIRIT WAS WITH GOD WHEN HE CREATED THE HEAVENS AND THE EARTH.

    TRUE ____ FALSE____

3. GOD THE FATHER WILL GIVE YOU THE HOLY SPIRIT, IF YOU ASK.

    TRUE ____ FALSE____

4. THE HOLY SPIRIT DOESN'T KNOW MY MIND AND HEART.

    TRUE ____ FALSE____

5. THE HOLY SPIRIT IS GOD.

    TRUE ____ FALSE____

111

COLOR THE PICTURE

WHAT IS GOD'S CHARACTER?
WHAT IS HE LIKE?
CONTINUE ON TO FIND OUT!

TWICE THE FUN

UNSCRAMBLE THE UNDERLINED WORDS IN THE VERSE BELOW. THEN, ON THE NEXT PAGE, FIND AND CIRCLE THEM IN THE WORD SEARCH PUZZLE.

"YOURS, O LORD, IS THE GREATNESS AND THE RPEOW AND THE YGRLO AND THE MAJESTY AND THE SPLENDOR, FOR EVERYTHING IN NHEEAV AND HETAR IS SYRUO. YOURS, O LORD, IS THE KMDOIDNG; YOU ARE EXALTED AS DHAE OVER ALL. WEALTH AND HONOR COME FROM UYO; YOU ARE THE REURL OF ALL STGHNI. IN YOUR HANDS ARE STRENGTH AND POWER TO EXALT AND EGVI STRENGTH TO ALL."

— — — — —   — — — — —

— — — — — —   — — — — —

— — — — —   — — — — — — —

— — — —   — — —   — — — — —

— — — — — —   — — — —

GOD IS KING OF THE UNIVERSE.

CONT'D ON THE NEXT PAGE...

```
K S V B T R U L E R
Y I Q T K J B V S T
G B N V S Y Q Y Y H
S I T G L O R Y O I
T B V Y D U P V U N
V Q S E B O K Y R G
H B T Q W S M Y S S
E S H E A V E N B V
A B R V Q K Y J S T
D V T B S E A R T H
```

AMAZING MAZES

SOMETIMES, LIFE CAN SEEM LIKE A MAZE AND IT IS HARD TO FIND THE WAY. IT IS GOOD TO KNOW THAT WE ARE ALWAYS IN GOD'S HAND AND HE KNOWS THE WAY WE SHOULD GO.

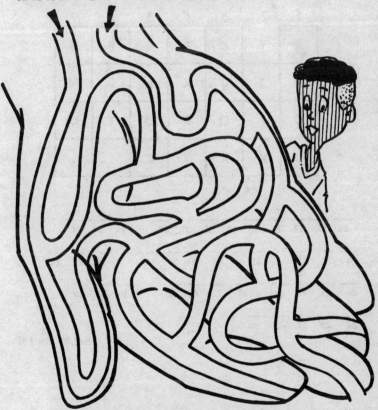

ALL THINGS ARE IN HIS HAND.
HE IS IN CONTROL OF MY LIFE.

CODE BUSTER

USE THE CODE CHART BELOW TO COMPLETE THE VERSE. CHOOSE FROM THE LEFT SET OF NUMBERS FIRST. (Eg: 23=J)

	1	2	3	4	5	6	7
1	A	B	C	D	E	F	G
2	H	I	J	K	L	M	N
3	O	P	Q	R	S	T	U
4	V	W	X	Y	Z		

"___ ___ ___ ___ ___ ___ ___ ___ ___   ___ ___ ___
34 22 17 21 36 15 31 37 35   11 34 15

___ ___ ___,   ___   ___ ___ ___ ___,   ___ ___ ___
44 31 37   31   25 31 34 14   11 27 14

___ ___ ___ ___   ___ ___ ___ ___   ___ ___ ___
44 31 37 34   25 11 42 35   11 34 15

___ ___ ___ ___ ___."
34 22 17 21 36

PSALM 119:137

GOD IS RIGHTEOUS.
HE CANNOT SIN AGAINST ME.

ZANY CODE BUSTER

TO DECODE THIS MYSTERY VERSE, LOOK AT EACH LETTER AND WRITE THE ONE THAT COMES <u>BEFORE</u> IT IN THE ALPHABET.

A B C D E F G H I J K L M N O P Q R
S T U V W X Y Z

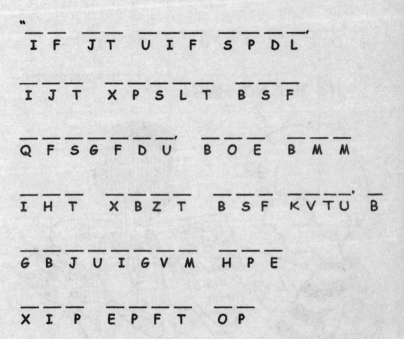

" __ __ ___ ___ ____ ,
  I F   J T   U I F   S P D L

___ ____ ___
I J T   X P S L T   B S F

_____ , ___ ___
Q F S G F D U   B O E   B M M

___ ____ ___ ____ . _
I H T   X B Z T   B S F   K V T U   B

_____ ___
G B J U I G V M   H P E

____ ___
X I P   E P F T   O P

GOD IS JUST.

CONT'D ON THE NEXT PAGE...

CONT'D FROM THE PREVIOUS PAGE.

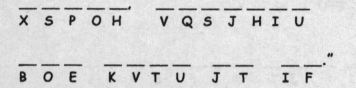

```
_____,  _____
X S P O H   V Q S J H I U

____ _____ ___ ___."
B O E  K V T U  J T  I F
```

DEUTERONOMY 32:4

IT'S JUST NOT FAIR!

REPORT CARD
1ST TERM
MATH D
SCIENCE C-
ENGLISH C
PHY ED
PILL F

DID IT EVER OCCUR TO YOU THAT IF ONE...STUDIES..?

HE WILL ALWAYS BE FAIR WITH ME.

ZANY CODE BUSTER

USE THE CODE CHART BELOW TO DECODE THE MYSTERY VERSE.

GOD IS LOVE.

CONT'D ON THE NEXT PAGE...

1 JOHN 4:8

HE WANTS TO HELP ME GET THE MOST
OUT OF LIFE.

UNSCRAMBLE AND ANSWER

FIRST, UNSCRAMBLE THE WORDS AND WRITE
THEM IN THE SPACES UNDER EACH WORD. THEN
LIST ALL THE CIRCLED LETTERS BELOW AND
UNSCRAMBLE THEM TO COMPLETE THE
STATEMENT.

"EHT   LEATNER   DGO   SI

___ __O_____ ____ _

RYOU   EFEGRFU   ADN

_O__ _O____ __O

HUTNADEENR   ERA

_____O____ ___

HET   GENEIRVTLSA   SARM."

_O_ __O_____ ____

DEUTERONOMY 33:27

GOD IS ⃝⃝⃝⃝⃝⃝⃝.

THE PLAN HE IS WORKING OUT FOR ME
IS EVERLASTING

121

FINISH THE VERSE

TO FIND OUT WHAT THE VERSE BELOW SAYS, FILL IN THE BLANKS. ALL THE CONSONANTS ARE THERE, SO ALL YOU NEED TO DO IS ADD THE VOWELS.

VOWELS: A E I O U

"__ L__RD, Y__ __ H__V __

S__ __RCH__D M__ __ND Y__ __

KN__W M__. Y__ __ KN__W WH__N __

S__T __ND WH__N __ R__ S__; Y__ __

P__RC__ __V__ MY TH__ __GHTS FR__M

__F__R. Y__ __ D__SC__RN MY G__ __NG

__ __T __ND MY LY__NG D__WN;

Y__ __ __RE F__M__L__ __R W__TH

__LL MY W__YS. B__F__R__ __ W__RD

__S __N MY T__NG__ __

GOD IS ALL KNOWING.

CONT'D ON THE NEXT PAGE...

CONT'D FROM THE PREVIOUS PAGE.

Y_ _ KN_W _T C_MPL_T_LY,
_ L_RD. Y_ _ H_M M_ _N —
B_H_ND _ND B_F_R_; Y_ _
H_V_ L_ _D Y_ _R H_ND _P_N
M_."

PSALM 139:1-5

HE KNOWS ALL ABOUT ME AND MY SITUATION
AND HOW TO WORK IT OUT FOR GOOD.

HIDDEN ALPHABET

FIND AND CIRCLE EVERY LETTER OF THE ALPHABET
THAT HAS BEEN HIDDEN IN THIS PICTURE AND
FINISH THE SENTENCE BELOW.

GOD KNOWS THE WAY
I __ __ __ __ __ __ GO.

FINISH THE PICTURE

USING THE GRID, DRAW THE PICTURE BELOW ON
THE FOLLOWING PAGE.

FROM THE PREVIOUS PAGE, USE THE GRID TO
DRAW THE PICTURE FOR YOURSELF.

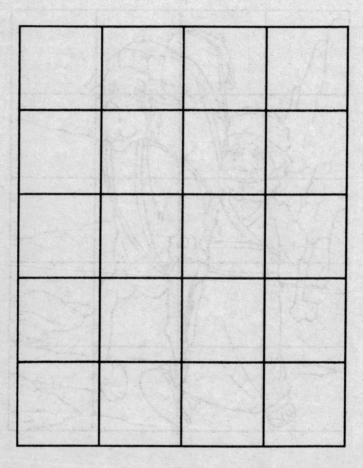

UNSCRAMBLE THE VERSE

TO FIND OUT WHAT THE VERSE BELOW SAYS, FILL
IN THE BLANKS. ALL THE VOWELS ARE THERE, SO
ALL YOU NEED TO ADD ARE THE CONSONANTS.

"REWEH NCA I OG OMRF UROY IITSPR? HEWER CAN I
ELFE RFMO OYRU SCPENERE? FI I OG PU OT HET
VNHEESA OYU EAR RTEHE; FI I EMAK YM DBE NI
THE TDESPH, OYU RAE EEHRT. FI I ESRI NO EHT
NIGWS FO ETH WDNA, FI I TELTES NO ETH ARF
IEDS FO HET EAS, VNEE REEHT YRUO NADH WILL
IEGDU EM, UYRO HITRG ADHN LWLI DOHL EM STFA."

"_ _ E _ E _ A _   I _ O _ _ O _

_ O U _   _ _ I _ I _? _ _ E _ E

_ A _ I _ _ E E _ _ O _ _ O U _

_ _ E _ E _ _ E? I _ I _ O U _

_ O _ _ E _ E A _ E _ _ _ O U

A _ E _ _ E _ E; I _ I _ A _ E

_ Y _ E _ I _ _ _ E _ E _ _ _ _,

_ O U A _ E _ _ E _ E.

CONT'D ON THE NEXT PAGE...

127

CONT'D FROM THE PREVIOUS PAGE.

I_ I _I_E O_ __E

_I___ O_ __E _A__,

I_ I _E___E O_ __E

_A_ _I_E O_ __E _EA,

E_E_ __E_E _OU_ _A__

_I__ _UI_E _E, _OU_

_I___ _A__ _I__ _O__

_E _A__."

PSALM 139:7-10

GOD IS EVERYWHERE.
THERE IS NO PLACE I CAN GO THAT HE
WILL NOT TAKE CARE OF ME.

128

ZANY CODE BUSTER

USE THE CODE CHART BELOW TO DECODE THE MYSTERY VERSE.

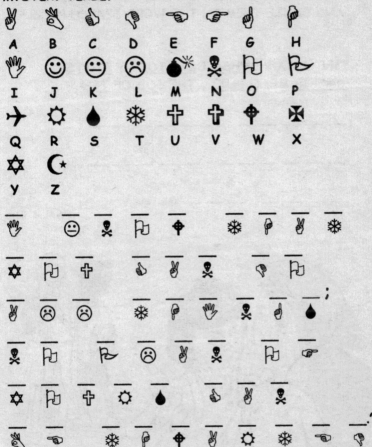

GOD IS ALL POWERFUL.
THERE IS NOTHING HE CAN'T DO ON MY
BEHALF.

TWICE THE FUN

UNSCRAMBLE THE UNDERLINED WORDS IN THE VERSE BELOW. THEN, ON THE NEXT PAGE, FIND AND CIRCLE THEM IN THE WORD SEARCH PUZZLE.

"INTO YOUR <u>DNHSA</u> I <u>MCMTOI</u> MY <u>RIIPTS</u> ; <u>DMEEER</u> ME, O <u>DLRO</u> , THE GOD OF <u>TTHUR</u> ."

_ _ _ _ _ _   _ _ _ _ _ _ _

_ _ _ _ _ _   _ _ _ _ _ _

_ _ _ _   _ _ _ _ _ _

PSALM 31:5

CONT'D ON THE NEXT PAGE...

```
S  V  H  D  J  R  B  S
L  T  R  U  T  H  G  P
O  S  D  E  H  S  V  I
R  J  B  G  D  N  R  R
D  H  V  N  L  E  D  I
G  R  A  Q  J  S  E  T
B  H  D  S  V  R  H  M
C  O  M  M  I  T  J  D
```

GOD IS TRUTH.
GOD CANNOT LIE TO ME.

AMAZING MAZES

AS YOU GO THROUGH THE MAZE, COLLECT THE LETTERS AND COMPLETE THE VERSE BELOW.

"I THE LORD DO NOT __ __ __ __ __ __ ."

MALACHI 3:6

GOD IS UNCHANGING.

SQUARE GAME

COLOR IN THE AREAS THAT HAVE A SQUARE TO COMPLETE THE STATEMENT BELOW.

I CAN DEPEND ON __ __ __ !

FILL IN THE BLANKS

WORD LIST:

FEAR	HOLY
GLORY	WORSHIP
NAME	RIGHTEOUS

"WHO WILL NOT __ __ __ __ YOU, O LORD

AND BRING __ __ __ __ __ TO YOUR __ __ __ __?

FOR YOU ALONE ARE __ __ __ __. ALL

NATIONS WILL COME AND

__ __ __ __ __ __ __ BEFORE YOU, FOR YOUR

__ __ __ __ __ __ __ __ __ ACTS HAVE BEEN

REVEALED."

REVELATION 15:4

WORD SEARCH

FIND AND CIRCLE THE WORDS BELOW IN THE
WORD SEARCH PUZZLE. LOOK UP, DOWN, FORWARD,
AND DIAGONALLY TO SOLVE THIS ONE!

```
C F L X Z L V P K G I J Y Z
P K V G L O R Y F Z X E L C
L F X Z C F G I J Y K T P V
V G A K D P I L Z C X E L F
F L C I X Z P A D G K R J V
V J P K T C F W G D Z N X L
L U F X Z H G S D K C A P V
C S V P K G F D J Z X L L F
F T Z X L D J U Y G K P V C
X V C P K G J Y L D F L Z X
R O C K L X Z D C G K P V F
Z V P K F G J Y Z J D C X L
C F L X G K P V Z F A R M S
Z V P D W Z Y J G K X L F C
X J K L F C R E F U G E P V
```

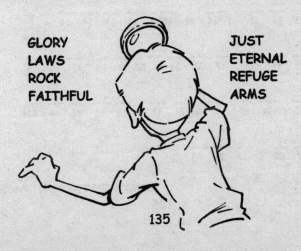

GLORY
LAWS
ROCK
FAITHFUL

JUST
ETERNAL
REFUGE
ARMS

135

CODE BUSTER

USE THE CODE CHART BELOW TO COMPLETE THE VERSE. CHOOSE FROM THE LEFT SET OF NUMBERS FIRST. (Eg: 23=J)

	1	2	3	4	5	6	7
1	A	B	C	D	E	F	G
2	H	I	J	K	L	M	N
3	O	P	Q	R	S	T	U
4	V	W	X	Y	Z		

"

K N O W   T H E R E F O R E
24 27 31 42   36 21 15 34 15 16 31 34 15

T H A T   T H E   L O R D
36 21 11 36   36 21 15   25 31 34 14

Y O U R   G O D   I S   G O D ;
44 31 37 34   17 31 14   22 35   17 31 14

H E   I S   T H E   F A I T H -
21 15   22 35   36 21 15   16 11 22 36 21

F U L   G O D
16 37 25   17 31 14

CONT'D ON THE NEXT PAGE...

___ ___ ___ ___ ___ ___ ___   ___ ___ ___
24 15 15 32 22 27 17   21 22 35

___ ___ ___ ___ ___ ___ ___ ___   ___ ___   ___ ___ ___ ___
13 31 41 15 27 11 27 36   31 16   25 31 41 15

___ ___   ___ ___ ___ ___ ___ ___ ___ ___ ___
36 31   11 36 21 31 37 35 11 27 14

___ ___ ___ ___ ___ ___ ___ ___ ___ ___ ___   ___ ___
17 15 27 15 34 11 36 22 31 27 35   31 16

___ ___ ___ ___ ___   ___ ___ ___   ___ ___ ___ ___
36 21 31 35 15   42 21 31   25 31 41 15

___ ___ ___   ___ ___ ___   ___ ___ ___ ___   ___ ___ ___
21 22 26   11 27 14   24 15 15 32   21 22 35

___ ___ ___ ___ ___ ___ ___ ___ "
13 31 26 26 11 27 14 35 .

DEUTERONOMY 7:9

GOD IS HOLY.
HE WILL BE HOLY IN ALL HE DOES.

137

•DOT 2 DOT•

CONNECT THE DOTS

WHEN YOU PRAY, YOU CAN ALWAYS COUNT ON GOD'S CHARACTER!

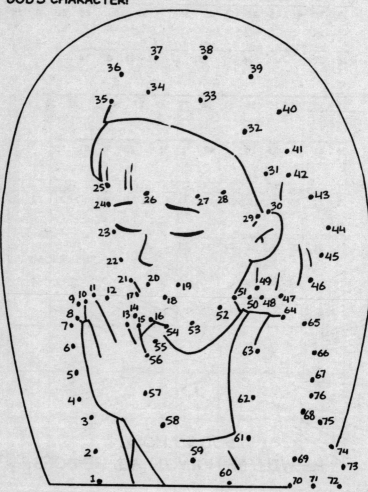

138

FINISH THE PICTURE

USING THE GRID, COMPLETE THE PICTURE BY
DUPLICATING THE FINISHED HALF ONTO THE
UNFINISHED AREA. ONE SQUARE HAS ALREADY
BEEN STARTED FOR YOU.

JESUS IS NOBLE OF CHARACTER.
JESUS, THE LION OF JUDAH!

COLOR THE SCROLL
GOD'S CHARACTER

GOD IS KING OF THE UNIVERSE

GOD IS RIGHTEOUS

GOD IS JUST

GOD IS LOVE

GOD IS ETERNAL

GOD IS ALL KNOWING

GOD IS EVERYWHERE

GOD IS ALL POWERFUL

GOD IS TRUTH

GOD IS UNCHANGEABLE

GOD IS FAITHFUL

GOD IS HOLY

COLOR THE PICTURE

WHO I AM IN CHRIST...
FORGIVEN!

141

UNSCRAMBLE AND ANSWER

FIRST, UNSCRAMBLE THE WORDS AND WRITE THEM IN THE SPACES UNDER EACH WORD. THEN LIST ALL THE CIRCLED LETTERS BELOW AND UNSCRAMBLE THEM TO COMPLETE THE STATEMENT.

"RRETFEOEH, CINSE EW EHVA

_____ ____ __

ENBE TFIDEJISU GRUHTOH

____ _____ _____

THFIA, EW EVHA CPEAE TIWH

_____ __ ____ _____ ____

ODG UTGHORH URO ROLD

____ _____ ___ ____

SUEJS RCITHS."

____ ____

ROMANS 5:1

I HAVE ⃝⃝⃝⃝⃝ WITH GOD.

142

FILL IN THE BLANKS

WORD LIST:

BLAMELESS   SIGHT
WORLD   CREATION
HOLY   CHOSE

"FOR HE _ _ _ _ _ US IN HIM BEFORE

THE _ _ _ _ _ _ _ _ OF THE

_ _ _ _ _ TO BE _ _ _ _ AND

_ _ _ _ _ _ _ _ _ IN HIS

_ _ _ _ _."

EPHESIANS 1:4

I AM ACCEPTED BY GOD!

UNSCRAMBLE THE VERSE

TO FIND OUT WHAT THE VERSE BELOW SAYS, FILL IN THE BLANKS. ALL THE VOWELS ARE THERE, SO ALL YOU NEED TO ADD ARE THE CONSONANTS.

"ETY OT LAL OWH EEVRIEC MHI OT SEHTO HOW LVEEBIE NI SHI EAMN, EH EVGA HET HRTIG OT OEMBOC RIEHNCLD FO OGD. . ."

"_E_ _O A__ ___O

_E_EI_E _I_, _O ___O_E

___O _E_IE_E I_ _I_

_A_E, _E _A_E ___E

_I___ _O _E_O_E

__I___E_ O_ _O_."

JOHN 1:12

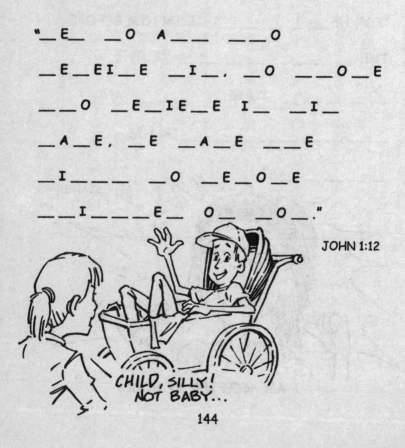

CHILD, SILLY!
NOT BABY...

WORD SEARCH

FIND AND CIRCLE THE WORDS BELOW IN THE
WORD SEARCH PUZZLE. LOOK UP, DOWN, FORWARD
AND DIAGONALLY TO SOLVE THIS ONE!

```
B H L G K C F T J D Q Z Y V
D W O R S H I P B K C L F G
C F G L T C L D Z J V E W X
H Q B J Y K V F G D V C T L
I G D L Y T W J K I B Z Q Y
L F K Z H D C G E T J L V B
D J Q G Y B R C T F C J K G
R L I K G P E A C E F D B O
E S B C F R A L G K J Z T D
N K D T J Q T B F Y C F D L
B Z F L C K I G D A V T W J
Q Y V T D G O L K B I C Q F
J L K Z C F N J T Y D T G K
C T F B G L D K F J C Z H T
K E T E R N A L L G F J B C
```

PEACE
FAITH
RECEIVE
HOLY
ETERNAL

SIGHT
CHILDREN
CREATION
GOD
WORSHIP

145

LOOK-ALIKES

FIND AND CIRCLE TWELVE DIFFERENCES IN THE TWO PICTURES BELOW.

FINISH THE VERSE

TO FIND OUT WHAT THE VERSE BELOW SAYS, FILL
IN THE BLANKS. ALL THE CONSONANTS ARE THERE,
SO ALL YOU NEED TO DO IS ADD THE VOWELS.

VOWELS: A E I O U

"D__N'T Y___ KN__W TH__T

Y___ Y___RS__LV__S __R__

G__D'S T__MPL__ __ND TH__T

G__D'S SP__R__T L__V__S

__N Y___?"

1 CORINTHIANS 3:16

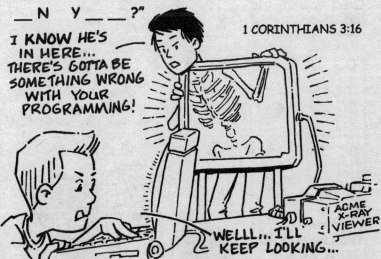

I KNOW HE'S __
IN HERE...
THERE'S GOTTA BE
SOMETHING WRONG
WITH YOUR
PROGRAMMING!

ACME
X-RAY
VIEWER

WELLL... I'LL
KEEP LOOKING...

I HAVE THE HOLY SPIRIT INSIDE ME!

ZANY CODE BUSTER

USE THE CODE CHART BELOW TO DECODE THE MYSTERY VERSE.

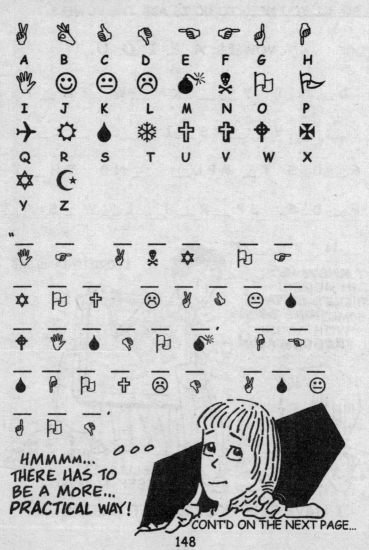

HMMMM...
THERE HAS TO
BE A MORE...
PRACTICAL WAY!

CONT'D ON THE NEXT PAGE...

CONT'D FROM THE PREVIOUS PAGE.

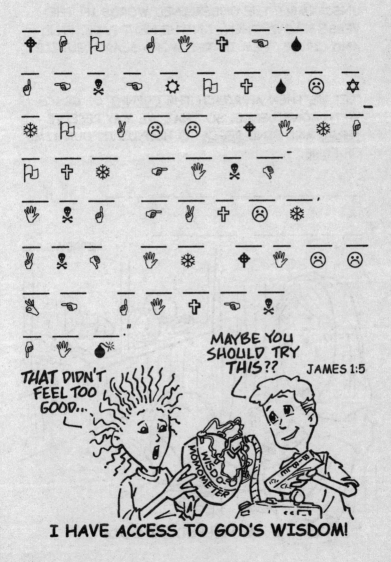

I HAVE ACCESS TO GOD'S WISDOM!

TWICE THE FUN

UNSCRAMBLE THE UNDERLINED WORDS IN THE VERSE BELOW. THEN, ON THE NEXT PAGE, FIND AND CIRCLE THEM IN THE WORD SEARCH PUZZLE.

"LET US THEN APPROACH THE <u>ORENHT</u> OF GRACE WITH CONFIDENCE, SO THAT WE MAY RECEIVE <u>YERMC</u> AND FIND <u>REGCA</u> TO HELP US IN OUR TIME OF <u>EDNE</u>."

_ _ _ _ _ _ _ _ _ _ _ _ _

_ _ _ _ _ _ _ _ _ _

HEBREWS 4:16

I AM HELPED BY GOD!

CONT'D ON THE NEXT PAGE...

```
S Q D W G L Z M
K T H R O N E G
F R N P Y C B M
A L H E A R F E
P X O R D J N R
R N G K F Q V C
I F P S N R D Y
N E E D R F P J
```

HIDDEN ALPHABET

FIND AND CIRCLE EVERY LETTER OF THE ALPHABET THAT HAS BEEN HIDDEN IN THIS PICTURE AND FINISH THE SENTENCE BELOW.

I RECEIVE _ _ _ _ _ BECAUSE OF GOD'S GRACE.

AMAZING MAZES

FIND THE WAY TO THE THRONE OF GRACE.

CODE BUSTER

USE THE CODE CHART BELOW TO COMPLETE THE VERSE. CHOOSE FROM THE LEFT SET OF NUMBERS FIRST. (Eg: 23=J)

	1	2	3	4	5	6	7
1	A	B	C	D	E	F	G
2	H	I	J	K	L	M	N
3	O	P	Q	R	S	T	U
4	V	W	X	Y	Z		

"
27 31 36   31 27 25 44   22 35   36 21 22 35

35 31 '   12 37 36   42 15   11 25 35 31

34 15 23 31 22 13 15   22 27   17 31 14

36 21 34 31 37 17 21   31 37 34   25 31 34 14

23 15 35 37 35   13 21 34 22 35 36 ,

CONT'D ON THE NEXT PAGE...

— — — — — — —   — — — —
36 21 34 31 37 17 21   42 21 31 26

— — — — — — — —   — — —
42 15   21 11 41 15   27 31 42

— — — — — — —
34 15 13 15 22 41 15 14

— — — — — — — — — — — — — —
34 15 13 31 27 13 22 25 22 11 36 22 31 27

ROMANS 5:11

HEY... WHAT IN THE WORLD DOES... REC... RECO... RECON-WHATEVER MEAN...?

"RECONCILE"? IT MEANS TO BE MADE "FRIENDS WITH AGAIN". SO WE'RE MADE FRIENDS AGAIN WITH GOD!

CHILDREN BIBLE

HMMPH... COOL!

I AM RECONCILED TO GOD!

ZANY CODE BUSTER

TO DECODE THIS MYSTERY VERSE, LOOK AT EACH LETTER AND WRITE THE ONE THAT COMES <u>BEFORE</u> IT IN THE ALPHABET.

A B C D E F G H I J K L M N O P Q R S T U V W X Y Z

" _ _ _ _ _ _ _ _ _ ' _ _ _ _ _
  U I F S F G P S F   U I F S F

_ _ _ _ _ _ _ _ _ _ _ _ _ -
J T O P X O P D P O E F N

_ _ _ _ _ _ _ _ _ _ _ _ _
O B U J P O G P S U I P T F

_ _ _
X I P

CONT'D ON THE NEXT PAGE...

___ ___ ___   ___ ___   ___ ___ ___ ___ ___
 B   S   F   J   O   D   I   S   J   T   U

___ ___ ___ ___."
 K   F   T   V   T

WHAT ABOUT, CON...
CON-DEM-NATION?
WHAT DOES
THAT MEAN?

TO BE
CONVICTED   ROMANS 8:1
AS GUILTY. TO BE JUDGED...
TO BE BLAMED, CRITICIZED,
DOOMED, SEN...

OKAY, OKAY!
I GET IT...

WOW! THANKS TO
JESUS... THAT'LL
NEVER HAPPEN
TO US!

WAY
COOLER
EVEN!

THERE IS NO CONDEMNATION FOR ME!

PICTURE FRAMES

WHAT COULD THE PICTURE BE?

DRAW EXACTLY WHAT IS IN EACH NUMBERED
FRAME AT THE TOP OF THE PAGE INTO EACH FRAME
OF THE SAME NUMBER IN THE GRID BELOW.

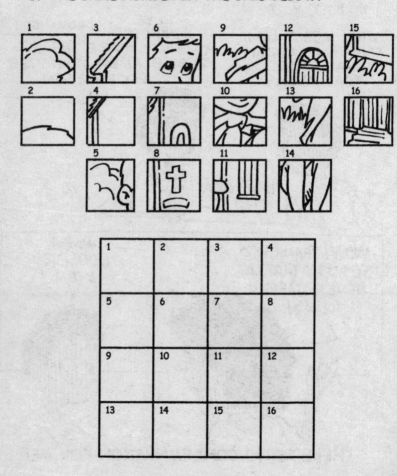

•••DOT 2 DOT•••

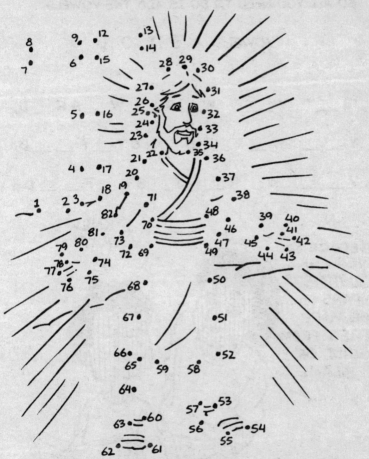

CONNECT THE DOTS

THERE IS *NO* CONDEMNATION FOR THOSE WHO ARE IN JESUS CHRIST!

FINISH THE VERSE

TO FIND OUT WHAT THE VERSE BELOW SAYS, FILL IN THE BLANKS. ALL THE CONSONANTS ARE THERE, SO ALL YOU NEED TO DO IS ADD THE VOWELS.

VOWELS: A E I O U

"B _ T Y _ _ W _ R _ W _ SH _ D,

Y _ _ W _ R _ S _ NCT _ F _ _ D,

Y _ _ W _ R _ J _ ST _ F _ _ D

_ N

BEFORE YOU EVEN ASK... "JUSTIFIED" MEANS TO BE MADE FREE FROM GUILT OR BLAME

I KNEW THAT!

CONT'D ON THE NEXT PAGE...

TH_ N_M_ _F TH_

L_RD J_S_S CHR_ST

_ND BY TH_ SP_R_T _F

__R G_D."

1 CORINTHIANS 6:11

WORD SEARCH

CROSS OUT EVERY LETTER THAT APPEARS FOUR TIMES IN THE PUZZLE TO FIND THE WORD THAT COMPLETES THE SENTENCE.

```
D O B T N R K S
R F J Z P C G X
S K B G X H X B
N E C H D F J P
J P Z X V B Z S
H F N R T T G C
K Z G C S P F H
L D T J K N R D
```

BECAUSE OF HIS GREAT _ _ _ _ FOR US, JESUS PAID THE PRICE FOR ALL OUR SINS!

162

LOOK-ALIKES

FIND AND CIRCLE TEN DIFFERENCES IN THE TWO PICTURES BELOW.

CODE BUSTER

USE THE CODE CHART BELOW TO COMPLETE THE VERSE. CHOOSE FROM THE LEFT SET OF NUMBERS FIRST. (Eg: 23=J)

	1	2	3	4	5	6	7
1	A	B	C	D	E	F	G
2	H	I	J	K	L	M	N
3	O	P	Q	R	S	T	U
4	V	W	X	Y	Z		

"
___ ___ ___   ___ ___ ___ ___   ___ ___ ___   ___ ___ ___
17 31 14   26 11 14 15   21 22 26   42 21 31

___ ___ ___   ___ ___   ___ ___ ___   ___ ___   ___ ___
21 11 14   27 31   35 22 27   36 31   12 15

___ ___ ___   ___ ___ ___   ___ ___ ' ___ ___
35 22 27   16 31 34   37 35   35 31

___ ___ ___ ___   ___ ___   ___ ___ ___
36 21 11 36   22 27   21 22 26

CONT'D ON THE NEXT PAGE...

CONT'D FROM THE PREVIOUS PAGE.

___ ___ ___ ___ ___ ___ ___   ___ ___ ___ ___ ___ ___
42 15   26 22 17 21 36   12 15 13 31 26 15

___ ___ ___ ___ ___ ___ ___ ___ ___ ___ ___ -
36 21 15   34 22 17 21 36 15 31 37 35

___ ___ ___ ___ ___ ___ ___ ___ ___ . "
27 15 35 35   31 16   17 31 14

2 CORINTHIANS 5:21

JUST SO YOU KNOW...
"RIGHTEOUSNESS" ALSO
MEANS TO BE "FREE OF
GUILT"...TO BE SEEN
AS RIGHTEOUS IN
GOD'S EYES!

MMPHH...
MMPHH...
MMPHH...
MMPHH...

I HAVE HIS RIGHTEOUSNESS!

165

FILL IN THE BLANKS

WORD LIST:

APPEAL   AMBASSADORS
CHRIST'S   WE
GOD   US

"__ __ ARE THEREFORE __ __ __ __ __ __'__ __ __ __ __ __ __ __ __ __ __ __ , AS

THOUGH __ __ __ WERE MAKING HIS

__ __ __ __ __ __ THROUGH __ __ ."

2 CORINTHIANS 5:20

DO YOU Need GOD? YOU BET YOU DO!

I AM GOD'S REPRESENTATIVE!

FINISH THE PICTURE

USING THE GRID, COMPLETE THE PICTURE BY
DUPLICATING THE FINISHED HALF ONTO THE
UNFINISHED AREA. ONE SQUARE HAS ALREADY
BEEN STARTED FOR YOU.

TWICE THE FUN

UNSCRAMBLE THE UNDERLINED WORDS IN THE VERSE BELOW. THEN, ON THE NEXT PAGE, FIND AND CIRCLE THEM IN THE WORD SEARCH PUZZLE.

"IF WE <u>EFCSOSN</u> OUR <u>SNSI</u>, HE IS <u>FFLUIAHT</u> AND <u>SUTJ</u> AND WILL <u>VGEROFI</u> US OUR SINS AND <u>RPIYFU</u> US FROM ALL UNRIGHTEOUSNESS."

_____ _____

_____

_____ _____

1 JOHN 1:9

CONT'D ON THE NEXT PAGE...

```
L J U S T B E P
S C H M I V W U
I S B K I N L R
N M X G C H S I
S H R W S T K F
B O L C V R B Y
F A I T H F U L
L C O N F E S S
```

I HAVE TO ADMIT... THIS WAY IS BETTER!

I AM COMPLETELY FORGIVEN!

ZANY CODE BUSTER

USE THE CODE CHART BELOW TO DECODE THE MYSTERY VERSE.

"

CONT'D ON THE NEXT PAGE...

CONT'D FROM THE PREVIOUS PAGE.

FINISH THE PICTURE

USING THE GRID, DRAW THE PICTURE BELOW ON THE FOLLOWING PAGE.

GOD'S LOVE IS SO AWESOME!

FROM THE PREVIOUS PAGE, USE THE GRID TO
DRAW THE PICTURE FOR YOURSELF.

ZANY CODE BUSTER

TO DECODE THIS MYSTERY VERSE, LOOK AT EACH LETTER AND WRITE THE ONE THAT COMES <u>BEFORE</u> IT IN THE ALPHABET.

A B C D E F G H I J K L M N O P Q R
S T U V W X Y Z

" __ __ __ __ __   __ __ __ __ __   __ __ __
  J I B W F   M P W F E   Z P V

__ __ __ __   __ __   __ __ __ __ __ __ __ -
 X J U I B O F W F S M B T U

__ __ __   __ __ __ __ ."
 J O H M P W F

JEREMIAH 31:3

I AM TENDERLY LOVED!

174

UNSCRAMBLE THE VERSE

TO FIND OUT WHAT THE VERSE BELOW SAYS, FILL IN THE BLANKS. ALL THE VOWELS ARE THERE, SO ALL YOU NEED TO ADD ARE THE CONSONANTS.

"OFR EW REA OT OGD HET OAMRA FO ITHCRS MAGNO HETSO HWO EAR NBIGE VADSE NAD TESHO HOW REA HGIIPRESN."

"__O__ __E A__E __O __O__

__E A__O__A O__ ____I__

A__O__ ___O__E __O A__E

__EI__ __A_E_ A__

__O__E __O A__E __E_I__-

I__."

_____ 2 CORINTHIANS 2:15

I AM A SWEET SMELL OF CHRIST TO GOD!

175

FINISH THE VERSE

TO FIND OUT WHAT THE VERSE BELOW SAYS, FILL IN THE BLANKS. ALL THE CONSONANTS ARE THERE, SO ALL YOU NEED TO DO IS ADD THE VOWELS.

VOWELS: A E I O U

"F _ R W _ _ _ R _ TH _

T _ MPL _ _ F TH _ L _ V _ NG

G _ D."

2 CORINTHIANS 6:16

YOU KNOW, HAREEM...
WE *REALLY* NEED
TO TALK ...

I AM THE TEMPLE OF GOD!

CODE BUSTER

USE THE CODE CHART BELOW TO COMPLETE THE VERSE. CHOOSE FROM THE LEFT SET OF NUMBERS FIRST. (Eg: 23=J)

	1	2	3	4	5	6	7
1	A	B	C	D	E	F	G
2	H	I	J	K	L	M	N
3	O	P	Q	R	S	T	U
4	V	W	X	Y	Z		

```
"
__ __ __    __ __ __    __ __    __ __ __
12 37 36    27 31 42    21 15    21 11 35

__ __ __ __ __ __ __ __ __ __    __ __ __
34 15 13 31 27 13 22 25 15 14    44 31 37

__ __    __ __ __ __ __ __'__    __ __ __ -
12 44    13 21 34 22 35 36  35   32 21 44

__ __ __ __ __    __ __ __ __
35 22 13 11 25    12 31 14 44
```

CONT'D ON THE NEXT PAGE...

177

___ ___ ___ ___ ___ ___ ___   ___ ___ ___ ___ ___
36 21 34 31 37 17 21   14 15 11 36 21

___ ___   ___ ___ ___ ___ ___ ___ ___   ___ ___ ___
36 31   32 34 15 35 15 27 36   44 31 37

___ ___ ___ ___   ___ ___   ___ ___ ___   ___ ___ ___ ___ ___ ;
21 31 25 44   22 27   21 22 35   35 22 17 21 36

___ ___ ___ ___ ___ ___ ___   ___ ___ ___ ___ ___ ___ ___
42 22 36 21 31 37 36   12 25 15 26 22 35 21

___ ___ ___   ___ ___ ___ ___   ___ ___ ___ ___
11 27 14   16 34 15 15   16 34 31 26

___ ___ ___ ___ ___ ___ ___ ___ ___ ___ . "
11 13 13 37 35 11 36 22 31 27

I CAN'T SEEM TO FIND MY CHOCO-CANDY-CARAMEL-FRUITY-BEAR PUFFS!?

COLOSSIANS 1:22

WELL... EH-HMMPH... DON'T BLAME ME !

I AM BLAMELESS AND BEYOND REPROACH!

COLOR THE PICTURE

ATTITUDE MAKES THE DIFFERENCE!

MY DAILY ATTITUDE ACTION PLAN

ZANY CODE BUSTER

USE THE CODE CHART BELOW TO DECODE THE
MYSTERY VERSE.

I WILL TALK TO GOD EVERY DAY

UNSCRAMBLE THE VERSE

TO FIND OUT WHAT THE VERSE BELOW SAYS, FILL IN THE BLANKS. ALL THE VOWELS ARE THERE, SO ALL YOU NEED TO ADD ARE THE CONSONANTS.

"MMITOC UYRO SWYA OT EHT RODL; UTTRS NI IHM DAN EH LLWI... EMKA ROYU TEEHSRSIGUOSN NIHES EILK HET WDAN."

"_ O _ _ I _ _   _ O U _   _ A _ _   _ O

_ _ E   _ O _ _ ;   _ _ U _ _   I _

_ I _   A _ _   _ E   _ I _ _ ...

_ A _ E   _ O U _   _ I _ _ _ _ E O U _ -

_ E _ _   _ _ I _ E   _ I _ E   _ _ E

_ A _ _ ."

PSALM 37:5-6

I WILL COMMIT MY WAYS TO THE LORD

181

FINISH THE PICTURE

USING THE GRID, DRAW THE PICTURE BELOW ON THE FOLLOWING PAGE.

"ALTITUDE" DEPENDS ON YOUR ATTITUDE!

FROM THE PREVIOUS PAGE, USE THE GRID TO
DRAW THE PICTURE FOR YOURSELF.

FINISH THE VERSE

TO FIND OUT WHAT THE VERSE BELOW SAYS, FILL IN THE BLANKS. ALL THE CONSONANTS ARE THERE, SO ALL YOU NEED TO DO IS ADD THE VOWELS.

VOWELS: A E I O U

"TH__S __S TH__ D__Y TH__

L__RD H__S M__D__: L__T

__S R__J____C__ __ND B__

GL__D __N __T."

PSALM 118:24

I WILL MAKE TODAY MY BEST DAY

EEW...!

I WILL MAKE TODAY MY BEST DAY

184

CODE BUSTER

USE THE CODE CHART BELOW TO COMPLETE THE
VERSE. CHOOSE FROM THE LEFT SET OF NUMBERS
FIRST. (Eg: 23=J)

	1	2	3	4	5	6	7
1	A	B	C	D	E	F	G
2	H	I	J	K	L	M	N
3	O	P	Q	R	S	T	U
4	V	W	X	Y	Z		

"

__ __ __ __ __ __ __ __
42 21 11 36 15 41 15 34

__ __ __ __ __ __ __ , __ __ __ __ __ __ __
21 11 32 32 15 27 35   13 31 27 14 37 13 36

__ __ __ __ __ __ __ __ __ __ __ __ __
44 31 37 34 35 15 25 41 15 35 22 27 11

__ __ __ __ __ __ __ __ __ __ __ __ __ __
26 11 27 27 15 34 42 31 34 36 21 44 31 16

__ __ __ __ __ __ __ __ __ __ __
36 21 15 17 31 35 32 15 25 31 16

__ __ __ __ __ __ . "
13 21 34 22 35 36

PHILIPPIANS 1:27

185

TWICE THE FUN

UNSCRAMBLE THE UNDERLINED WORDS IN THE VERSE BELOW. THEN, ON THE NEXT PAGE, FIND AND CIRCLE THEM IN THE WORD SEARCH PUZZLE.

"BE <u>NIDK</u> AND COMPASSIONATE TO <u>EON</u> ANOTHER, FORGIVING EACH OTHER, <u>SJTU</u> AS IN <u>SRIHTC</u> GOD <u>VRAFGEO</u> YOU."

___ ____ _____

_____ ____ _____

EPHESIANS 4:32

CONT'D ON THE NEXT PAGE...

```
D  F  R  C  K  B  H  R
K  F  B  H  C  L  Z  J
R  C  O  N  E  K  F  U
B  C  H  R  I  S  T  S
K  H  R  F  G  C  K  T
Z  I  K  C  B  A  F  R
F  R  N  H  K  L  V  C
Y  C  K  D  F  R  B  E
```

I WILL BE KIND TO OTHERS

PICTURE FRAMES

WHAT COULD THE PICTURE BE?

DRAW EXACTLY WHAT IS IN EACH NUMBERED
FRAME AT THE TOP OF THE PAGE INTO EACH FRAME
OF THE SAME NUMBER IN THE GRID BELOW.

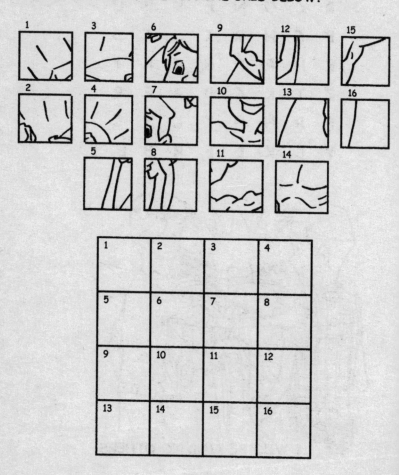

ZANY CODE BUSTER

TO DECODE THIS MYSTERY VERSE, LOOK AT EACH LETTER AND WRITE THE ONE THAT COMES <u>BEFORE</u> IT IN THE ALPHABET.

A B C D E F G H I J K L M N O P Q R
S T U V W X Y Z

" _ _ _ _ _ _ _ _ _ _ _ _ _ _ -
  J   D B O   E P   F W F S Z

_ _ _ _ _ _ _ _ _ _ _ _ _
U I J O H   U I   S P V H I

_ _ _ _ _ _ _ _ _ _ _ _ _
I J N   X I P   H J W F T   N F

_ _ _ _ _ _ _ _ ."
T U S F O H U I

PHILIPPIANS 4:13

I WILL DO WHAT I'M ASKED WITHOUT
COMPLAINT

189

UNSCRAMBLE THE VERSE

TO FIND OUT WHAT THE VERSE BELOW SAYS, FILL IN THE BLANKS. ALL THE VOWELS ARE THERE, SO ALL YOU NEED TO ADD ARE THE CONSONANTS.

"EB VYRE FCLAERU, ETNH, WHO OUY EVIL—TON SA WUESIN TUB SA EIWS, NGIKAM HET TOMS FO RYEEV NTIYURTPOPO, SEBCEUA ETH SDYA RAE LIVE."

"_E _E___ _A_E_U_,

__E_, _O_ _OU _I_E—

_O_ A_ U__I_E _U_ A_

_I_E, _A_I__ ___E

_O__ O_ E_E___ O__O_-

_U_I__, _E_AU_E __E

_A__ A_E E_I_."

EPHESIANS 5:15-16

I WILL MAKE THE MOST OF EVERY OPPORTUNITY

MULTIPLE CHOICE

CIRCLE THE CORRECT ANSWER.

1. WE SHOULD PUT OUR TRUST IN:
   - A. MONEY
   - B. THE LORD
   - C. FRIENDS

2. WHAT MUST WE SEEK TO BE GIVEN ALL THINGS?
   - A. A JOB
   - B. A RAISE IN OUR ALLOWANCE
   - C. GOD'S KINGDOM

3. EVERYONE WHO HAS WILL BE GIVEN:

   MATTHEW 25:29

   - A. A REALLY COOL BIKE
   - B. MORE, AND HE WILL HAVE AN ABUNDANCE
   - C. NOTHING! YOUR ROOM'S TOO CROWDED ANYWAYS!

I WILL USE MY TALENTS EVERY DAY

ZANY CODE BUSTER

USE THE CODE CHART BELOW TO DECODE THE MYSTERY VERSE.

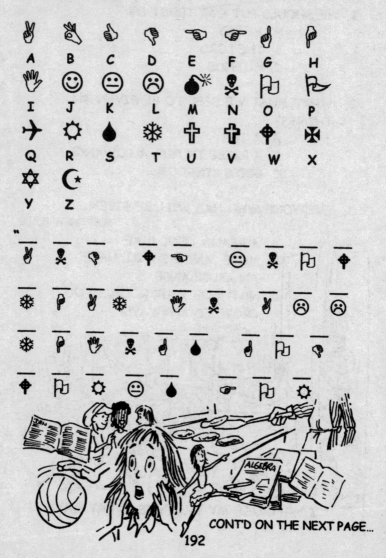

CONT'D ON THE NEXT PAGE...

ROMANS 8:28

I WILL TRUST GOD TO WORK EVERYTHING OUT

FILL IN THE BLANKS

WORD LIST:

HELPFUL	BENEFIT
NEEDS	UNWHOLESOME
ACCORDING	LISTEN
TALK	MOUTHS

" DO NOT LET ANY _ _ _ _ _ _ _ _ _ -

_ _ _ _   _ _ _ _ COME OUT OF YOUR

_ _ _ _ _ _ _ . BUT ONLY WHAT IS

_ _ _ _ _ _ _ _ FOR BUILDING OTHERS

UP

HEY...
YA' DOIN'
THOSE STUPID
DRAWINGS
AGAIN..?

CONT'D ON THE NEXT PAGE...

_ _ _ _ _ _ _ _ _ _ _ _ TO THEIR

_ _ _ _ _ _ _, THAT IT MAY _ _ _ _ _ -

_ _ _ _ THOSE WHO _ _ _ _ _ _ _ ."

EPHESIANS 4:29

I WILL ENCOURAGE OTHERS TO BE ALL GOD
CREATED THEM TO BE

195

CODE BUSTER

USE THE CODE CHART BELOW TO COMPLETE THE VERSE. CHOOSE FROM THE LEFT SET OF NUMBERS FIRST. (Eg: 23=J)

	1	2	3	4	5	6	7
1	A	B	C	D	E	F	G
2	H	I	J	K	L	M	N
3	O	P	Q	R	S	T	U
4	V	W	X	Y	Z		

"
14 31   27 31 36   12 15   11 27 43 22 31 37 35

11 12 31 37 36   11 27 44 36 21 22 27 17 ,

12 37 36   22 27   15 41 15 34 44 36 21 22 27 17

12 44   32 34 11 44 15 34

CONT'D ON THE NEXT PAGE...

196

___ ___ ___   ___ ___ ___ ___ ___ ___ ___ , ___ ___ ___ ___
11 27 14   32 15 36 22 36 22 31 27   42 22 36 21

___ ___ ___ ___ ___ ___ ___ ___ ___ ___ ___ ,
36 21 11 27 24 35 17 22 41 22 27 17

___ ___ ___ ___ ___ ___ ___   ___ ___ ___ ___
32 34 15 35 15 27 36   44 31 37 34

___ ___ ___ ___ ___ ___ ___ ___   ___ ___   ___ ___ ___ . "
34 15 33 37 15 35 36 35   36 31   17 31 14

PHILIPPIANS 4:6

DON'T PANIC...
THIS IS
SUPPOSED TO
BE FUN!

I WILL NOT PANIC...I WILL PRAY

197

COLOR THE COMIC

CONT'D ON THE NEXT PAGE...

CONT'D ON THE NEXT PAGE...

200

ANSWER PAGES

FINISH THE VERSE

FINISH THE VERSE BY MATCHING THEM WITH THE PHRASES ON THE FOLLOWING PAGE.

1. "IN THE BEGINNING GOD CREATED..."

   THE HEAVENS AND THE EARTH.

   GENESIS 1:1

2. "AND GOD SAID 'LET THERE BE LIGHT.'"

   AND THERE WAS LIGHT.

   GENESIS 1:3

3. "AND GOD SAID 'LET THERE BE AN EXPANSE BETWEEN.'"

   THE WATERS TO SEPERATE WATER FROM WATER

   GENESIS 1:6

4. "SO GOD MADE AN EXPANSE AND SEPARATED."

   THE WATER UNDER THE EXPANSE FROM THE WATER ABOVE IT.

   GENESIS 1:7

5. "AND IT WAS SO GOD CALLED THE..."

   EXPANSE SKY

   GENESIS 1:8

6. "AND GOD SAID 'LET THE WATER UNDER THE SKY...'"

   BE GATHERED TO ONE PLACE AND LET DRY GROUND APPEAR

   GENESIS 1:9

2

FINISH THE VERSE

TO FIND OUT WHAT THE VERSE BELOW SAYS FILL IN THE BLANKS. ALL THE CONSONANTS ARE THERE SO ALL YOU NEED TO DO IS ADD THE VOWELS.

VOWELS A E I O U

"G O D   C A L L E D   TH E   DRY

G R O U N D   'L A N D'   A N D   TH E

G A TH E R E D   W A T E R S   H E

C A L L E D   'S E A S'   A N D   G O D

S A W   TH A T   I T   W A S

G O O D."

GENESIS 1:10

4

FILL IN THE BLANKS

WORD LIST

VEGETATION
LAND
THEIR
PLANTS

SEED
TREES
KINDS
FRUIT

THEN GOD SAID " LET THE **L A N D**

PRODUCE **V E G E T A T I O N**

SEED-BEARING **P L A N T S** AND

T R E E S ON THE LAND THAT BEAR

F R U I T WITH **S E E D** IN IT

ACCORDING TO **T H E I R** VARIOUS

KINDS."

GENESIS 1:11

5

TWICE THE FUN

UNSCRAMBLE THE UNDERLINED WORD IN EACH VERSE THEN ON THE OPPOSITE PAGE FIND AND CIRCLE IT IN THE WORD SEARCH PUZZLE.

1. "AND GOD SAID ' LET THERE BE LIGHTS IN THE EXPANSE OF THE SKY TO SEPARATE THE DAY FROM NIGHT."

   GENESIS 1:14

2. "GOD MADE TWO GREAT LIGHTS - THE GREATER LIGHT TO GOVERN THE DAY AND THE LESSER LIGHT TO GOVERN THE NIGHT HE ALSO MADE THE STARS."

   GENESIS 1:16

3. "SO GOD CREATED THE GREAT CREATURES OF THE SEA AND EVERY LIVING AND MOVING THING WITH WHICH THE WATER TEEMS ACCORDING TO THEIR KINDS AND EVERY WINGED BIRD ACCORDING TO ITS KIND."

   GENESIS 1:21

6

[Word Search]

```
L M I N I G H T
I Y K E S B O Z
G B A M O V I N G
H M S N N S C U
T R E O D D A Y
G A S R O I O
L I V I N G S I
F E Y B J K S W
```

7

ZANY CODE BUSTER

USE THE CODE CHART BELOW TO DECODE THE MYSTERY VERSE

[code chart symbols A–Z]

A N D   **G O D**

S A I D   **L E T**

T H E   **A N D**

T   **T**

CONT'D ON THE NEXT PAGE...

8

GENESIS 1:24

9

ZANY CODE BUSTER

TO DECODE THIS MYSTERY VERSE LOOK AT EACH LETTER AND WRITE THE ONE THAT COMES **BEFORE** IT IN THE ALPHABET.

A B C D E F G H I J K L M N O P Q R
S T U V W X Y Z

T H E N   N O   G O D   D I D
U I F   O P   H P E   E J U

S A I D   D E M   L E T   T U
U M N   E N N   A K F   U V

M A N   A N D   A L J   N E W
N A O   O N E   B M K   O F X

O U R   U R S   N O W   N E T
P V S   V S T   O P X   O F U

I M A G E   A G E   N E O
N A H F   H F U   O F P

10

O U R   L I K E.
P V S   M J L F

N E S S-
O F T T

DUCK!

GENESIS 1:29

11

CODE BUSTER

USE THE CODE CHART BELOW TO COMPLETE THE VERSE. CHOOSE FROM THE LEFT SET OF NUMBERS FIRST. (Eg 23-3)

	1	2	3	4	5	6
1	A	B	C	D	E	F
2	G	H	I	J	K	L	M	N
3	O	P	Q	R	S	T	U
4	V	W	X	Y	Z

S O   G O D
3 5 3 7 3 7 7 5

C R E A T E D   M A N
1 3 3 4 1 4 1 6 1   1 6 1

I N   H I S   O W N
2 3 2 4 2 2 3 3 4 2

I M A G E   O F   T H E
2 3 2 1 2 7 3 7 3 6 7

I M A G E   O F   G O D
2 3 2 1 2 7 3 7 3 7 3

H E   C R E A T E D
2 6 1 3 3 4 1 4 1

H I M
2 4 2

GENESIS 1:27

12

• • DOT 2 DOT • •

CONNECT THE DOTS

ADAM

13

UNSCRAMBLE THE VERSE

TO FIND OUT WHAT THE VERSE BELOW SAYS, FILL IN THE BLANKS. ALL THE VOWELS ARE THERE SO ALL YOU NEED TO ADD ARE THE CONSONANTS

B C D F G H J K L M N P Q R S T V W X Y Z

"HETN HET OLRD GOD DREA A WMNAO NFOR HTE BER BH DHA ETAKN TOU FO MNA."

T H E N   T H E   L O R D
G O D   M A D E   A
W O M A N   F R O M   T H E
R I B   H E   H A D
T A K E N   O U T   O F
M A N.

GENESIS 2:22

14

FINISH THE PICTURE

THIS PICTURE LOOKS A LITTLE UNFINISHED, DOESN'T IT? A LOT OF THINGS ARE LEFT OUT SO WHY DON'T YOU FINISH IT BY FILLING IN AS MANY MISSING PIECES AS YOU CAN FIND

15

LOOK-ALIKES

FIND AND CIRCLE SIX DIFFERENCES IN THE TWO PICTURES BELOW

16

AMAZING MAZES

AS YOU GO THROUGH THE MAZE COLLECT THE LETTERS AND COMPLETE THE STATEMENT BELOW

GOD IS OUR C R E A T O R

17

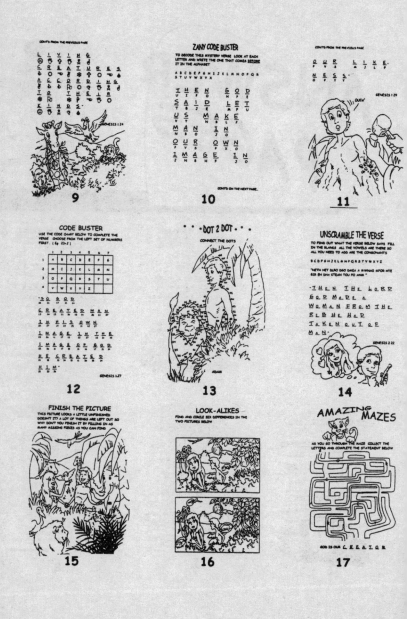

°°°SQUARE GAME°°°

COLOR IN THE AREAS THAT HAVE A SQUARE TO COMPLETE THE VERSE BELOW

"GOD SAW ALL THAT HE HAD MADE, AND IT WAS VERY _G_ _O_ _O_ _D_."

GENESIS 1:31

18

PICTURE FRAMES
WHAT COULD THE PICTURE BE??

DRAW EXACTLY WHAT IS IN EACH NUMBERED FRAME AT THE TOP OF THE PAGE INTO EACH FRAME OF THE SAME NUMBER IN THE GRID BELOW

19

PICTURE FRAMES
WHAT COULD THE PICTURE BE??

DRAW EXACTLY WHAT IS IN EACH NUMBERED FRAME AT THE TOP OF THE PAGE INTO EACH FRAME OF THE SAME NUMBER IN THE GRID BELOW

20

TRUE / FALSE

1. THE FIRST THING GOD CREATED WAS THE TREES

   TRUE ____ FALSE _X_

2. GOD SPOKE ALL CREATION INTO EXISTENCE

   TRUE _✓_ FALSE ____

3. MAN CREATED WOMAN

   TRUE ____ FALSE _X_

4. WE ARE CREATED IN THE IMAGE OF GOD

   TRUE _✓_ FALSE ____

5. GOD NAMED ALL THE ANIMALS

   TRUE ____ FALSE _X_

21

WORD SEARCH

CROSS OUT EVERY LETTER THAT APPEARS AT LEAST FOUR TIMES IN THE PUZZLE TO FIND THE WORD THAT COMPLETES THE SENTENCE

GOD THE _____

22

UNSCRAMBLE THE VERSE

TO FIND OUT WHAT THE VERSE BELOW SAYS FILL IN THE BLANKS. ALL THE VOWELS ARE THERE SO ALL YOU NEED TO ADD ARE THE CONSONANTS

B C D F G H J K L M N P Q R S T V W X Z

"A _HTFAE OT HTE HRE_ATSELS _ FRGDEMEE FO DWSOEW SI GOD NI SEH YHLO WENDRLEL."

"A _F_A_T_H_E_R_ _T_O_ _T_H_E_ _F_A_T_H_E_R_L_E_S_S_ _A_ _D_E_F_E_N_D_E_R_ _O_F_ _W_I_D_O_W_S_ _I_S_ _G_O_D_ _I_N_ _H_I_S_ _H_O_L_Y_ _D_W_E_L_L_I_N_G_."

PSALM 68:5

23

CODE BUSTER

USE THE CODE CHART BELOW TO COMPLETE THE VERSE. CHOOSE FROM THE LEFT SET OF NUMBERS FIRST (EG 23=Z)

	1	2	3	4	5	6	7
1	A	B	C	D	E	F	G
2	H	I	J	K	L	M	N
3	O	P	Q	R	S	T	U
4	V	W	X	Y	Z		

_H_E_ _W_I_L_L_ _C_A_L_L_ _O_U_T_

_T_O_ _M_E_ _Y_O_U_ _A_R_E_ _M_Y_

_F_A_T_H_E_R_ _M_Y_ _G_O_D_

_T_H_E_ _R_O_C_K_ _M_Y_

_S_A_V_I_O_U_R_

24

AMAZING MAZES

ADAM AND EVE ARE PLAYING HIDE AND SEEK. BUT THE GARDEN IS SO BIG THAT ADAM IS HAVING A HARD TIME FINDING EVE. CAN YOU HELP HIM FIND THE WAY?

25

TWICE THE FUN

UNSCRAMBLE THE UNDERLINED WORDS IN THE VERSE THEN ON THE OPPOSITE PAGE FIND AND CIRCLE THEM IN THE WORD SEARCH PUZZLE

"BUT YOU ARE OUR _FATHER_ THOUGH ABRAHAM DOES NOT _KNOW_ US OR _ISRAEL_ ACKNOWLEDGE US YOU O _LORD_ ARE OUR FATHER OUR _REDEEMER_

_F_A_T_H_E_R_ _K_N_O_W_
_O_U_R_ _L_O_R_D_
_R_E_D_E_E_M_E_R_

ISAIAH 63:16

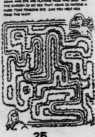

CONT'D ON THE NEXT PAGE.

26

...CONT'D FROM THE PREVIOUS PAGE.

27

ZANY CODE BUSTER

TO DECODE THIS MYSTERY VERSE LOOK AT EACH LETTER AND WRITE THE ONE THAT COMES BEFORE IT IN THE ALPHABET.

A B C D E F G H I J K L M N O P Q R
S T U V W X Y Z

__IN THE SAME WAY,__
JO UIF TBNF XBZ

__LET YOUR LIGHT__
MFU ZPVS MJHIU

__SHINE BEFORE MEN__
TIJOF CFGPSF NFO

__THAT THEY MAY__
UIBU UIFZ NBZ

__SEE YOUR GOOD__
TFF ZPVS HPPE

__DEEDS AND PRAISE__
EFFET BOE QSBJTF

...CONT'D ON THE NEXT PAGE.

28

...CONT'D FROM THE PREVIOUS PAGE.

__YOUR FATHER IN__
ZPVS GBUIFS JO

__HEAVEN__
IFBWFO

MATTHEW 5:48

29

ZANY CODE BUSTER

USE THE CODE CHART BELOW TO DECODE THE MYSTERY VERSE.

__LOOK AT THE__

__BIRDS OF THE AIR,__

__THEY DO NOT SOW__

...CONT'D ON THE NEXT PAGE.

32

...CONT'D FROM THE PREVIOUS PAGE.

__OR REAP OR STORE__

__AWAY IN BARNS, AND__

__YET YOUR HEAVENLY__

__FATHER FEEDS THEM__

__ARE YOU NOT MUCH__

__MORE VALUABLE THAN__

__THEY?__

MATTHEW 6:26

33

WORD SEARCH

FIND AND CIRCLE THE WORDS BELOW IN THE WORD SEARCH PUZZLE. LOOK UP, DOWN, FORWARD AND DIAGONALLY TO SOLVE THIS ONE!

FATHER
SON
DAUGHTER
CHILD

HEAVEN
GOD
LOVE
CARE

34

FINISH THE VERSE

TO FIND OUT WHAT THE VERSE BELOW SAYS FILL IN THE BLANKS. ALL THE CONSONANTS ARE THERE SO ALL YOU NEED TO DO IS ADD THE VOWELS.

VOWELS A E I O U

"I WILL BE A FATHER TO
YOU AND YOU WILL BE
MY SONS AND DAUGHTERS"

2 CORINTHIANS 6:18

35

UNSCRAMBLE AND ANSWER

FIRST UNSCRAMBLE THE WORDS AND WRITE THEM IN THE SPACE BELOW. THEN ON THE FOLLOWING PAGE LIST ALL THE CIRCLED LETTERS AND UNSCRAMBLE THEM TO SPELL OUT THE ANSWER TO THE QUESTION.

"ON EON SHA ENSE HTE HTRAFE
NO ONE HAS SEEN THE FATHER

CTEPXE HET EON HWO SI ROFM
EXCEPT THE ONE WHO IS FROM

DGO. NYOL EH SHA ENSE HTE
GOD. ONLY HE HAS SEEN THE

BOD. ONLY HE HAS SEEN ONE
FATHER"

JOHN 6:46

...CONT'D ON THE NEXT PAGE.

36

...CONT'D FROM THE PREVIOUS PAGE

(H)(F)(R)(A)(T)(E)

GOD IS OUR HEAVENLY F A T H E R!

37

FINISH THE VERSE
TO FIND OUT WHAT THE VERSE BELOW SAYS, FILL
IN THE BLANKS. ALL THE CONSONANTS ARE THERE
SO ALL YOU NEED TO DO IS ADD THE VOWELS

VOWELS A E I O U

"MY FATHER WHO HAS

GIVEN THEM TO ME IS

GREATER THAN ALL. NO

ONE CAN SNATCH THEM

OUT OF MY FATHER'S

HAND. I AND THE FATHER

ARE ONE."

JOHN 10:29-30

38

HIDDEN ALPHABET
FIND AND CIRCLE EVERY LETTER OF THE ALPHABET
THAT HAS BEEN HIDDEN IN THIS PICTURE

39

CODE BUSTER
USE THE CODE CHART BELOW TO COMPLETE THE
VERSE. CHOOSE FROM THE LEFT SET OF NUMBERS
FIRST (Eg 13=J)

JESUS SAID "DO

NOT HOLD ON TO

ME FOR I HAVE

NOT YET RETURNED

TO THE FATHER

CONT'D ON THE NEXT PAGE...

42

...CONT'D FROM THE PREVIOUS PAGE

GO INSTEAD TO MY

BROTHERS AND

TELL THEM 'I AM

RETURNING TO MY

FATHER AND YOUR

FATHER, TO MY GOD

AND YOUR GOD.'"

JOHN 20:17

43

WORD SEARCH
HOW MANY TIMES CAN YOU FIND THE WORD
FATHER IN THE WORD SEARCH PUZZLE BELOW.
LOOK UP, DOWN, FORWARD AND DIAGONALLY TO
SOLVE THIS ONE

44

SQUARE GAME
COLOR IN THE AREAS THAT HAVE A SQUARE TO
COMPLETE THE SENTENCE BELOW

GOD IS MY F A T H E R!

45

FILL IN THE BLANKS

WORD LIST	
LOVE	AM
HIM	PLEASED
THIS	HEAVEN
VOICE	SON

"AND A VOICE FROM HEAVEN

SAID THIS IS MY SON WHOM I

LOVE WITH HIM I AM WELL

PLEASED."

MATTHEW 3:17

47

FINISH THE VERSE
TO FIND OUT WHAT THE VERSE BELOW SAYS, FILL
IN THE BLANKS. ALL THE CONSONANTS ARE THERE
SO ALL YOU NEED TO DO IS ADD THE VOWELS

VOWELS A E I O U

"ALL THINGS HAVE BEEN

COMMITTED TO ME BY MY

FATHER. NO ONE KNOWS

THE SON EXCEPT THE

FATHER, AND NO ONE

KNOWS THE FATHER

CONT'D ON THE NEXT PAGE...

48

CONT'D FROM THE PREVIOUS PAGE

EXCEPT THE SON AND
THOSE TO WHOM THE
SON CHOOSES TO
REVEAL HIM.

MATTHEW 11:27

49

ZANY CODE BUSTER

TO DECODE THIS MYSTERY VERSE LOOK AT EACH
LETTER AND WRITE THE ONE THAT COMES BEFORE
IT IN THE ALPHABET.

A B C D E F G H I J K L M N O P Q R
S T U V W X Y Z

THEN THOSE IN
U I F O   U I P T F   J O

THE BOAT
U I F   C P B U

WORSHIPED HIM
X P S T I J Q F E   I J N

SAYING TRULY
T B Z J O H   U S V M Z

YOU ARE THE
Z P V   B S F   U I F

SON OF GOD
T P O   P G   H P E

MATTHEW 14:33

50

TWICE THE FUN

UNSCRAMBLE THE UNDERLINED WORDS IN EACH
VERSE THEN ON THE OPPOSITE PAGE FIND AND
CIRCLE THEM IN THE WORD SEARCH PUZZLE.

1 "SIMON PETER ANSWERED   YOU ARE THE
   RHITS   THE NSO OF THE LIVING ODG."

MATTHEW 16:16

CHRIST SON GOD

2 "A DUOC CAME FROM THE LROD, SAYING
   'THIS IS MY SON WHOM I HAVE CHOSEN
   TELNS TO HIM.'"

LUKE 9:35

VOICE CLOUD
LISTEN HIM

CONT'D ON THE NEXT PAGE.

52

CONT'D FROM THE PREVIOUS PAGE

53

WORD JUMBLE

FILL IN THE BLANK SPACES BY WRITING IN THE
OPPOSITE OF EACH WORD BELOW, ANSWERING
EACH CLUE CORRECTLY USING THE LETTERS IN THE
CIRCLES. COMPLETE THE SENTENCE BELOW.

MOTHER   F A T H E R

DAUGHTER S O N

DARK   L I G H T

END   B E G I N N I N G

NIGHT   D A Y

MAN   W O M A N

THE FATHER AND THE SON ARE BOTH .
G O D

54

WORD SEARCH

HOW MANY TIMES CAN YOU FIND THE WORD SON
BELOW IN THE WORD SEARCH PUZZLE. LOOK UP
DOWN, FORWARD AND DIAGONALLY TO SOLVE
THIS ONE!

55

UNSCRAMBLE AND ANSWER

FIRST UNSCRAMBLE THE WORDS AND WRITE
THEM IN THE SPACES UNDER EACH WORD. THEN
LIST ALL THE CIRCLED LETTERS BELOW AND
UNSCRAMBLE THEM TO SPELL OUT THE ANSWER TO
THE QUESTION.

"OFR SO OS VEOLD ETH
FOR G O D S O LOVED THE

LWDRO AHTT EH EGVA IHS
W O R L D THAT HE GAVE HIS

NEO GAN LOYN NSO"
O N E AND O N L Y S O N"

JOHN 3:16

WHO IS JESUS CHRIST?

G O D S   S O N

56

AMAZING MAZES

AS YOU GO THROUGH THE MAZE, COLLECT THE
LETTERS AND COMPLETE THE STATEMENT BELOW.

GOD L O V E S ME

57

FINISH THE VERSE

TO FIND OUT WHAT THE VERSE BELOW SAYS, FILL
IN THE BLANKS. ALL THE CONSONANTS ARE THERE
SO ALL YOU NEED TO DO IS ADD THE VOWELS

VOWELS A E I O U

"FATHER THE TIME HAS
COME GLORIFY YOUR
SON THAT YOUR SON
MAY GLORIFY YOU."

JOHN 17:1

58

WORD SEARCH

FIND AND CIRCLE THE WORDS BELOW IN THE WORD SEARCH PUZZLE. LOOK UP, DOWN, FORWARD AND DIAGONALLY TO SOLVE THIS ONE!

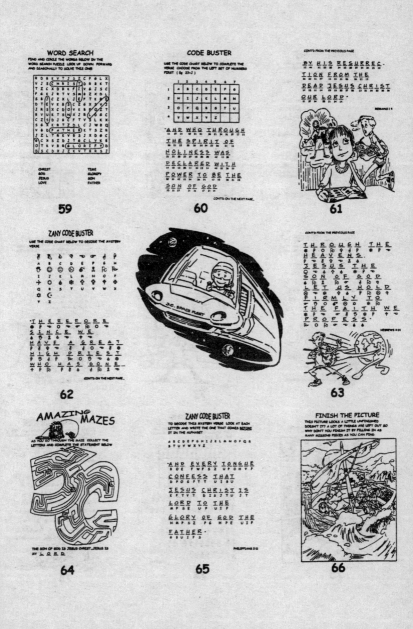

CHRIST
GOD
JESUS
LOVE

TRUE
GLORIFY
SON
FATHER

59

CODE BUSTER

USE THE CODE CHART BELOW TO COMPLETE THE VERSE. CHOOSE FROM THE LEFT SET OF NUMBERS FIRST (Eg 23=J)

"AND WHO THROUGH
THE SPIRIT OF
HOLINESS WAS
DECLARED WITH
POWER TO BE THE
SON OF GOD

CONT'D ON THE NEXT PAGE...

60

BY HIS RESURREC-
TION FROM THE
DEAD JESUS CHRIST
OUR LORD.

ROMANS 1:4

61

ZANY CODE BUSTER

USE THE CODE CHART BELOW TO DECODE THE MYSTERY VERSE

"THEREFORE
SINCE WE
HAVE A GREAT
HIGH PRIEST
WHO HAS GONE...

CONT'D ON THE NEXT PAGE...

62

THROUGH THE
HEAVENS,
JESUS THE
SON OF GOD
LET US HOLD
FIRMLY TO
THE FAITH WE
PROFESS.

HEBREWS 4:14

63

AMAZING MAZES

AS YOU GO THROUGH THE MAZE COLLECT THE LETTERS AND COMPLETE THE STATEMENT BELOW

THE SON OF GOD IS JESUS CHRIST...JESUS IS
MY L O R D .

64

ZANY CODE BUSTER

TO DECODE THIS MYSTERY VERSE LOOK AT EACH LETTER AND WRITE THE ONE THAT COMES BEFORE IT IN THE ALPHABET.

ABCDEFGHIJKLMNOPQR
STUVWXYZ

"AND EVERY TONGUE
BOE FWFSZ UPOHVF
CONFESS THAT
DPOGFTT UIBU
JESUS CHRIST IS
KFTVT DISJTU JT
LORD TO THE
MPSE UP UIF
GLORY OF GOD THE
HMPSZ PG HPE UIF
FATHER.
GBUIFS.

PHILIPPIANS 2:11

65

FINISH THE PICTURE

THIS PICTURE LOOKS A LITTLE UNFINISHED DOESN'T IT? A LOT OF THINGS ARE LEFT OUT SO WHY DON'T YOU FINISH IT BY FILLING IN AS MANY MISSING PIECES AS YOU CAN FIND.

66

UNSCRAMBLE THE VERSE

TO FIND OUT WHAT THE VERSE BELOW SAYS, FILL IN THE BLANKS. ALL THE VOWELS ARE THERE, SO ALL YOU NEED TO ADD ARE THE CONSONANTS.

* OE EONT UT2S 3A ON7 3CEEMYE 3E2U3 7ONE12 3A RLEO TUCNCEONE OT ELY2 NE 2N1 *

"2O IHEM 2U1I 12 YOU
RECEIVEM 2E2U2 CHRIST
12 LORD GOMTINUE IO
LIVE IN HIM."

COLOSSIANS 2:6

67

LOOK-ALIKES

FIND AND CIRCLE EIGHT DIFFERENCES IN THE TWO PICTURES BELOW

68

PICTURE FRAMES

WHAT COULD THE PICTURE BE??

DRAW EXACTLY WHAT IS IN EACH NUMBERED FRAME AT THE TOP OF THE PAGE INTO EACH FRAME OF THE SAME NUMBER IN THE GRID BELOW

69

UNSCRAMBLE THE VERSE

TO FIND OUT WHAT THE VERSE BELOW SAYS, FILL IN THE BLANKS. ALL THE VOWELS ARE THERE, SO ALL YOU NEED TO ADD ARE THE CONSONANTS.

* NEIIHEM INGHTE OEN HEITP, NEO HINHUNET NELE NE LAL ANRTOEICI LINLI EN LEAR OT AANESTTE AU OFNA ENT EVLO FO OGG ATNT 2E NE IRTHCI UAING URO SOLR *

"NEIIHER HEIGHT NOR
DEPTH NOR ANYTHING
ELSE IN ALL CREATION
WILL BE ABLE TO
SEPARATE US FROM

CONTD ON THE NEXT PAGE.

70

CONTD FROM THE PREVIOUS PAGE

THE LOVE OF GOD
THAT IS IN CHRIST
JESUS OUR LORD."

ROMANS 8:39

71

WORD SEARCH

CROSS OUT EVERY LETTER THAT APPEARS FOUR TIMES IN THE PUZZLE TO FIND THE WORD THAT COMPLETES THE SENTENCE

JESUS IS L O R D OF ALL!

72

FIND AND CIRCLE EVERY LETTER OF THE ALPHABET THAT HAS BEEN HIDDEN IN THIS PICTURE.

73

CODE BUSTER

USE THE CODE CHART BELOW TO COMPLETE THE VERSE. CHOOSE FROM THE LEFT SET OF NUMBERS FIRST (e.g. 22-J)

"AND WE HAVE SEEN
AND TESTIFY THAT
THE FATHER HAS
SENT HIS SON TO
BE SAVIOUR OF
THE WORLD."

1 JOHN 4:14

74

UNSCRAMBLE THE VERSE

TO FIND OUT WHAT THE VERSE BELOW SAYS, FILL IN THE BLANKS. ALL THE VOWELS ARE THERE, SO ALL YOU NEED TO ADD ARE THE CONSONANTS.

* OYU 6A LAL 2ON1 OF 6OR IHROUAH EIIH TROEGFE TENO IRTHCI AONN EROCULT EEVEIRENG. HUTE AELETN *

"YOU ARE ALL SONS OF
GOD THROUGH FAITH
IN CHRIST JESUS FOR
ALL OF YOU WHO WERE
BAPTIZED INTO CHRIST
HAVE CLOTHED YOUR-
SELVES WITH CHRIST"

GALATIANS 3:26,27

75

HIDDEN: ALPHABET

FIND AND CIRCLE EVERY LETTER OF THE ALPHABET THAT HAS BEEN HIDDEN IN THIS PICTURE. THEN USING THOSE LETTERS, COMPLETE THE STATEMENT BELOW.

I AM GOD'S C H I L D

78

FINISH THE VERSE

TO FIND OUT WHAT THE VERSE BELOW SAYS, FILL IN THE BLANKS. ALL THE CONSONANTS ARE THERE SO ALL YOU NEED TO DO IS ADD THE VOWELS.

VOWELS A E I O U

"NOW THE EARTH WAS FORMLESS AND EMPTY, DARKNESS WAS OVER THE SURFACE OF THE DEEP AND THE SPIRIT OF GOD WAS HOVERING OVER THE WATERS"

GENESIS 1:2

80

TWICE THE FUN

UNSCRAMBLE THE UNDERLINED WORDS IN EACH VERSE. THEN ON THE NEXT PAGE, FIND AND CIRCLE THEM IN THE WORD SEARCH PUZZLE.

1 "WHERE CAN I GO FROM YOUR TIRPIS?"
"WHERE CAN I FLEE FROM YOUR ENCERPES?"

SPIRIT PRESENCE

PSALMS 139:7

2 "I WILL ROUP OUT MY SPIRIT ON YOUR GNIRFFSPO."

POUR OFFSPRING

ISAIAH 44:3

3 "AND I HAVE DELLIF HER WITH THE SPIRIT OF DGO."

FILLED GOD

EXODUS 31:3

CONT'D ON THE NEXT PAGE...

81

CONT'D FROM THE PREVIOUS PAGE

82

CODE BUSTER

USE THE CODE CHART BELOW TO COMPLETE THE VERSE. CHOOSE FROM THE LEFT SET OF NUMBERS FIRST (1 by 2)

	1	2	3	4	5	6	7
1	A	B	C	D	E	F	G
2	H	I	J	K	L	A	N
3	O	P	Q	R	S	T	U
4	V	W	X	Y	Z		

"I BAPTIZE YOU
WITH WATER FOR
REPENTANCE BUT
AFTER ME WILL
COME ONE WHO IS

CONT'D ON THE NEXT PAGE...

83

CONT'D FROM THE PREVIOUS PAGE

MORE POWERFUL
THAN I WHOSE
SANDALS I AM NOT
FIT TO CARRY HE
WILL BAPTIZE YOU
WITH THE HOLY
SPIRIT AND FIRE"

MATTHEW 3:11

WHOAA!

84

UNSCRAMBLE THE VERSE

TO FIND OUT WHAT THE VERSE BELOW SAYS, FILL IN THE BLANKS. ALL THE VOWELS ARE THERE SO ALL YOU NEED TO ADD ARE THE CONSONANTS.

"IF YOU THEN THOUGH YOU ARE EVIL KNOW HOW TO GIVE GOOD GIFTS TO YOUR CHILDREN HOW MUCH MORE WILL YOUR FATHER IN HEAVEN GIVE THE HOLY SPIRIT TO THOSE WHO ASK HIM"

LUKE 11:13

85

AMAZING MAZES

THE HOLY SPIRIT WANTS TO COME TO YOU. GO THROUGH THE MAZE TO FIND THE PATH HE TAKES.

86

FILL IN THE BLANKS

WORD LIST
COUNSELOR
EVERYTHING
NAME
TEACH
REMIND
HOLY SPIRIT
FATHER
THINGS

"BUT THE COUNSELOR THE HOLY SPIRIT WHOM THE FATHER WILL SEND IN MY NAME WILL TEACH YOU ALL THINGS AND WILL REMIND YOU OF EVERYTHING I HAVE SAID TO YOU"

JOHN 14:26

87

° ° SQUARE GAME ° °

COLOR IN THE AREAS THAT HAVE A SQUARE TO FIND THE ANSWER TO COMPLETE THE VERSE BELOW

"BUT WHEN HE THE _S P I R I T_ OF TRUTH COMES HE WILL GUIDE YOU INTO ALL TRUTH."

JOHN 16 13

88

LOOK-ALIKES

FIND AND CIRCLE TEN DIFFERENCES IN THE TWO PICTURES BELOW

89

ZANY CODE BUSTER

USE THE CODE CHART BELOW TO DECODE THE MYSTERY VERSE

90

CONT'D ON THE NEXT PAGE...

...CONT'D FROM THE PREVIOUS PAGE

"FIND ANYTHING YET?"

ROMANS 8 27

91

FINISH THE PICTURE

THIS PICTURE LOOKS A LITTLE UNFINISHED DOESN'T IT? A LOT OF THINGS ARE LEFT OUT SO WHY DON'T YOU FINISH IT BY FILLING IN AS MANY MISSING PIECES AS YOU CAN FIND

92

AMAZING MAZES

AS YOU GO THROUGH THE MAZE COLLECT THE LETTERS AND COMPLETE THE VERSE BELOW

"BUT GOD HAS REVEALED IT TO US BY HIS _S P I R I T._ THE SPIRIT SEARCHES ALL THINGS, EVEN THE DEEP THINGS OF GOD."

I CORINTHIANS 2 10

93

CODE BUSTER

USE THE CODE CHART BELOW TO COMPLETE THE VERSE. CHOOSE FROM THE LEFT SET OF NUMBERS FIRST (Eg: 22=I)

	1	2	3	4	5	6	7
1	A	B	C	D	E	F	G
2	H	I	J	K	L	M	N
3	O	P	Q	R	S	T	U
4	V	W	X	Y	Z		

WE HAVE NOT

RECEIVED THE

SPIRIT OF THE

WORLD BUT THE

SPIRIT WHO IS-

CONT'D ON THE NEXT PAGE...

94

...CONT'D FROM THE PREVIOUS PAGE

FROM GOD THAT WE

MAY UNDERSTAND

WHAT GOD HAS

FREELY GIVEN

US.

I CORINTHIANS 2 12

GO AWAY! I'VE TOLD YOU BEFORE... I ALREADY HAVE THE ONLY SPIRIT I'LL EVER NEED!

95

FILL IN THE BLANKS

WORD LIST

RECEIVED	TEMPLE
KNOW	HOLY SPIRIT
YOU	GOD
BODY	YOUR

"DO YOU NOT K N O W THAT Y O U R

B O D Y IS A T E M P L E OF THE

H O L Y S P I R I T WHO IS IN

Y O U WHOM YOU HAVE

R E C E I V E D FROM G O D"

DOES ME
SEEM DIFFERENT
TO YOU, TODAY?

1 CORINTHIANS 6:9

96

UNSCRAMBLE AND ANSWER

FIRST UNSCRAMBLE THE WORDS AND WRITE
THEM IN THE SPACES UNDER EACH WORD THEN
LIST ALL THE CIRCLED LETTERS BELOW AND
UNSCRAMBLE THEM TO SPELLOUT THE ANSWER TO
THE QUESTION

"EH DAENTONI SU TAE

(W)E ANOINTED US SET

SHI LSEA FO POIWHNSER

HIS SEAL OF OWNE(R)SHIP

NO SU DAN TPU SHI TPSIIR

ON US (A)ND PUT HIS SPIRIT

NI RUO SHTERA SA A

IN OUR HEARTS AS A

CONT'D ON THE NEXT PAGE...

97

...CONT FROM PREVIOUS PAGE

.TDIESPO SGNUIZREEATN

DEPOSIT GUARAN(T)EEING

TWAH SI OT ECMO"

WHAT IS TO COM(E)"

2 CORINTHIANS 1:22

WHERE DOES THE HOLY SPIRIT LIVE?

IN MY H E A R T

98

PICTURE FRAMES

WHAT COULD THE PICTURE BE??

DRAW EXACTLY WHAT IS IN EACH NUMBERED
FRAME AT THE TOP OF THE PAGE INTO EACH FRAME
OF THE SAME NUMBER IN THE GRID BELOW

LOVE JOY
PEA

99

ZANY CODE BUSTER

USE THE CODE CHART BELOW TO DECODE THE
MYSTERY VERSE

BUT THE

FRUIT OF THE

SPIRIT

IS LOVE JOY

PEACE

CONT'D ON THE NEXT PAGE...

100

...CONT'D FROM THE PREVIOUS PAGE

KINDNESS

GOODNESS

FAITHFULNESS

GENTLENESS

AND SELF-

CONTROL

GALATIANS 5:22

I CAN
HAVE THEM
ALL??

101

WORD SEARCH

HOW MANY TIMES CAN YOU FIND THE WORD
HOLY SPIRIT BELOW IN THE WORD SEARCH
PUZZLE LOOK UP DOWN FORWARD BACKWARDS
AND DIAGONALLY TO SOLVE THIS ONE!!

102

• • DOT 2 DOT • •

CONNECT THE DOTS

106

LETTERS / ALPHABET PUZZLE / PICTURE!!

FIND AND CIRCLE EVERY LETTER OF THE ALPHABET
THAT HAS BEEN HIDDEN IN THIS PICTURE AND
FINISH THE SENTENCE BELOW

THE HOLY SPIRIT IS MY T E A C H E R

107

MULTIPLE CHOICE
CIRCLE THE CORRECT ANSWER

1. "IN THE BEGINNING GOD CREATED THE_
   A SEA
   B HEAVENS AND EARTH
   C APPLE TREE"

2. GOD MADE MAN IN THE IMAGE OF_
   A MONKEYS
   B MAN
   C GOD

3. GOD CREATED EVE OUT OF ADAM S_

   A RIB
   B ARM
   C TOE

CONT'D ON THE NEXT PAGE.

108

CONT'D FROM THE PREVIOUS PAGE

4. WE ARE CHILDREN OF_
   A GOD
   B ADAM
   C OUR PARENTS

5. WHEN JESUS CALLED GOD, "ABBA" HE WAS SAYING_
   A FATHER
   B CREATOR
   C LORD

6. WE BELIEVE IN_
   A ONE GOD
   B THREE GODS
   C ONE GOD IN THREE PERSONS

"YES! IT'S ALL SO CLEAR NOW! SHELL, YOLK, WHITE. THREE PARTS... BUT ALL ONE EGG!"

109

TRUE / FALSE

1. A VOICE CAME FROM HEAVEN AND SAID "THIS IS JESUS "
   TRUE ___ FALSE X

2. GOD CREATED EVE
   TRUE ✓ FALSE

3. JESUS CHRIST IS THE SON OF GOD
   TRUE ✓ FALSE

4. JESUS USED HIS GODLY POWERS DURING HIS MINISTRY
   TRUE ✓ FALSE

5. JESUS IS SAVIOUR OF THE WORLD
   TRUE ✓ FALSE

110

TRUE / FALSE

1. WE BECOME CHILDREN OF GOD BY GOING TO CHURCH
   TRUE ___ FALSE X

2. THE HOLY SPIRIT WAS WITH GOD WHEN HE CREATED THE HEAVENS AND THE EARTH
   TRUE ✓ FALSE

3. GOD THE FATHER WILL GIVE YOU THE HOLY SPIRIT IF YOU ASK
   TRUE ✓ FALSE

4. THE HOLY SPIRIT DOESN'T KNOW MY MIND AND HEART
   TRUE ___ FALSE X

5. THE HOLY SPIRIT IS GOD.
   TRUE ✓ FALSE

111

TWICE THE FUN
UNSCRAMBLE THE UNDERLINED WORDS IN THE VERSE BELOW THEN, ON THE NEXT PAGE, FIND AND CIRCLE THEM IN THE WORD SEARCH PUZZLE

"YOURS O LORD IS THE GREATNESS AND THE RPEOW AND THE YGLRO AND THE MAJESTY AND THE SPLENDOR FOR EVERYTHING IN NVEHAE AND HRTEA IS SYOUR YOURS, O LORD IS THE DMKNOIG YOU ARE EXALTED AS DHAE OVER ALL WEALTH AND HONOR COME FROM UOY YOU ARE THE RERLU OF ALL NIGSTH IN YOUR HANDS ARE STRENGTH AND POWER TO EXALT AND EGVI STRENGTH TO ALL."

POWER   GLORY
HEAVEN   EARTH
YOURS   KINGDOM
HEAD   YOU   RULER
THINGS   GIVE

1 CHRONICLES 29 11-12

GOD IS KING OF THE UNIVERSE.

CONT'D ON THE NEXT PAGE.

113

CONT'D FROM THE PREVIOUS PAGE.

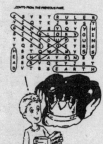

114

AMAZING MAZES

SOMETIMES LIFE CAN SEEM LIKE A MAZE AND IT IS HARD TO FIND THE WAY IT IS GOOD TO KNOW THAT WE ARE ALWAYS IN GOD S HAND AND HE KNOWS THE WAY WE SHOULD GO

ALL THINGS ARE IN HIS HAND
HE IS IN CONTROL OF MY LIFE.

115

CODE BUSTER

USE THE CODE CHART BELOW TO COMPLETE THE VERSE CHOOSE FROM THE LEFT SET OF NUMBERS FIRST (eg 23=J)

	1	2	3	4	5	6	7
1	A	B	C	D	E	F	G
2	H	I	J	K	L	M	N
3	O	P	Q	R	S	T	U
4	V	W	X	Y	Z		

RIGHTEOUS ARE
YOU O LORD AND
YOUR LAWS ARE
RIGHT

PSALMS 119 137

GOD IS RIGHTEOUS.
HE CANNOT SIN AGAINST ME

116

ZANY CODE BUSTER

TO DECODE THIS MYSTERY VERSE LOOK AT EACH LETTER AND WRITE THE ONE THAT COMES BEFORE IT IN THE ALPHABET

ABCDEFGHIJKLMNOPQR
STUVWXYZ

HE IS THE ROCK
IF JT UIF SPDL

HIS WORKS ARE
IJT XPSLT BSF

PERFECT AND ALL
QFSGFDU BOE BMM

HIS WAYS ARE JUST A
IJT XBZT BSF KVTUB

FAITHFUL GOD
GBJUIGVM HPE

WHO DOES NO_
XIP EPFT OP

GOD IS JUST.

CONT'D ON THE NEXT PAGE.

117

CONT'D FROM THE PREVIOUS PAGE

Panel 118

WRONG UPRIGHT

AND JUST IS HE

IT'S JUST NOT FAIR!

DEUTERONOMY 32:4

DID IT EVER OCCUR TO YOU THAT IF ONE...SNICKERS...?

HE WILL ALWAYS BE FAIR WITH ME.

118

ZANY CODE BUSTER

USE THE CODE CHART BELOW TO DECODE THE MYSTERY VERSE

WHOEVER

DOES NOT

LOVE DOES

NOT KNOW

GOD IS LOVE

CONT'D ON THE NEXT PAGE

119

CONT'D FROM THE PREVIOUS PAGE

Panel 120

GOD BECAUSE

GOD IS LOVE

1 JOHN 4:8

HE WANTS TO HELP ME GET THE MOST OUT OF LIFE.

120

UNSCRAMBLE AND ANSWER

FIRST UNSCRAMBLE THE WORDS AND WRITE THEM IN THE SPACES UNDER EACH WORD THEN LIST ALL THE CIRCLED LETTERS BELOW AND UNSCRAMBLE THEM TO COMPLETE THE STATEMENT

THT LEATNER DEO SI
THE ETERNAL GOD IS

RYOU EFERRPU ADN
YOUR REFUGE AND

HUTNADEENR ERA
UNDERNEATH ARE

HET GENEIRVTLSA SARRA
THE EVERLASTING ARMS

DEUTERONOMY 33:27

GOD IS ETERNAL

THE PLAN HE IS WORKING OUT FOR ME
IS EVERLASTING

121

FINISH THE VERSE

TO FIND OUT WHAT THE VERSE BELOW SAYS FILL IN THE BLANKS ALL THE CONSONANTS ARE THERE SO ALL YOU NEED TO ADD IS ADD THE VOWELS

VOWELS A E I O U

"O LORD YOU HAVE

SEARCHED ME AND YOU

KNOW ME YOU KNOW WHEN I

SIT AND WHEN I RISE YOU

PERCEIVE MY THOUGHTS FROM

AFAR YOU DISCERN MY GOING

OUT AND MY LYING DOWN

YOU ARE FAMILIAR WITH

ALL MY WAYS BEFORE A WORD

IS ON MY TONGUE

GOD IS ALL KNOWING

122

CONT'D FROM THE PREVIOUS PAGE

Panel 123

YOU KNOW IT COMPLETELY

O LORD YOU HEM ME IN-

BEHIND AND BEFORE YOU

HAVE LAID YOUR HAND UPON

ME"

HE KNOWS ALL ABOUT ME AND MY SITUATION
AND HOW TO WORK IT OUT FOR GOOD

123

HIDDEN ALPHABET

FIND AND CIRCLE EVERY LETTER OF THE ALPHABET THAT HAS BEEN HIDDEN IN THIS PICTURE AND FINISH THE SENTENCE BELOW

GOD KNOWS THE WAY
I SHOULD GO

124

UNSCRAMBLE THE VERSE

TO FIND OUT WHAT THE VERSE BELOW SAYS FILL IN THE BLANKS ALL THE VOWELS ARE THERE SO ALL YOU NEED TO ADD ARE THE CONSONANTS

WHERE CAN I GO FROM

YOUR SPIRIT? WHERE

CAN I FLEE FROM YOUR

PRESENCE? IF I GO UP

TO THE HEAVENS YOU

ARE THERE IF I MAKE

MY BED IN THE DEPTHS

YOU ARE THERE

CONT'D ON THE NEXT PAGE

127

...CONT'D FROM THE PREVIOUS PAGE

(128)

...IF I RISE ON THE
WINGS OF THE DAWN,
IF I SETTLE ON THE
FAR SIDE OF THE SEA,
EVEN THERE YOUR HAND
WILL GUIDE ME YOUR
RIGHT HAND WILL HOLD
ME FAST.

— PSALMS 139:9-10

GOD IS EVERYWHERE.
THERE IS NO PLACE I CAN GO THAT HE
WILL NOT TAKE CARE OF ME.

128

ZANY CODE BUSTER

USE THE CODE CHART BELOW TO DECODE THE
MYSTERY VERSE

I KNOW THAT
YOU CAN DO
ALL THINGS;
NO PLAN OF
YOURS CAN
BE THWARTED.

— JOB 42:2

GOD IS ALL POWERFUL.
THERE IS NOTHING HE CAN'T DO ON MY
BEHALF.

129

TWICE THE FUN

UNSCRAMBLE THE UNDERLINED WORDS IN THE
VERSE BELOW. THEN, ON THE NEXT PAGE, FIND
AND CIRCLE THEM IN THE WORD SEARCH PUZZLE

"INTO YOUR SHNDA I IMOCMT MY STIRIP
EEDREM ME O ROLD THE GOD OF THRUT."

HANDS COMMIT
SPIRIT REDEEM
LORD TRUTH

— PSALMS 31:5

CONT'D ON THE NEXT PAGE...

130

(131)

...CONT'D FROM THE PREVIOUS PAGE

(word search grid containing TRUTH, COMMIT)

GOD IS TRUTH.
GOD CAN NOT LIE TO ME

131

AMAZING MAZES

AS YOU GO THROUGH THE MAZE, COLLECT THE
LETTERS AND COMPLETE THE VERSE BELOW

"I THE LORD DO NOT C H A N G E."

— MALACHI 3:6

GOD IS UNCHANGING

132

SQUARE GAME

COLOR IN THE AREAS THAT HAVE A SQUARE TO
COMPLETE THE STATEMENT BELOW

I CAN DEPEND ON H I M!

133

FILL IN THE BLANKS

WORD LIST	
FEAR	HOLY
GLORY	WORSHIP
NAME	RIGHTEOUS

" WHO WILL NOT F E A R YOU O LORD
AND BRING G L O R Y TO YOUR N A M E ?
FOR YOU ALONE ARE H O L Y. ALL
NATIONS WILL COME AND
W O R S H I P BEFORE YOU FOR YOUR
R I G H T E O U S ACTS HAVE BEEN
REVEALED "

— REVELATION 15:4

134

WORD SEARCH

FIND AND CIRCLE THE WORDS BELOW IN THE
WORD SEARCH PUZZLE. LOOK UP, DOWN, FORWARD
AND DIAGONALLY TO SOLVE THIS ONE

(word search grid)

GLORY
LAWS
ROCK
FAITHFUL

JUST
ETERNAL
REFUGE
ARMS

135

CODE BUSTER

USE THE CODE CHART BELOW TO COMPLETE THE
VERSE. CHOOSE FROM THE LEFT SET OF NUMBERS
FIRST (Eg 23=1)

(code chart grid)

K N O W T H E R E F O R E
T H A T T H E L O R D
Y O U R G O D I S G O D
H E I S T H E F A I T H -
F U L G O D.

136

CONT'D FROM THE PREVIOUS PAGE

KEEPING HIS
COVENANT OF LOVE
TO A THOUSAND
GENERATIONS OF
THOSE WHO LOVE
HIM AND KEEP HIS
COMMANDS.

DEUTERONOMY 7:9

GOD IS HOLY.
HE WILL BE HOLY IN ALL HE DOES

137

• DOT 2 DOT •
CONNECT THE DOTS

WHEN YOU PRAY YOU CAN ALWAYS COUNT ON GOD'S CHARACTER

138

UNSCRAMBLE AND ANSWER

FIRST UNSCRAMBLE THE WORDS AND WRITE THEM IN THE SPACES UNDER EACH WORD THEN LIST ALL THE CIRCLED LETTERS BELOW AND UNSCRAMBLE THEM TO COMPLETE THE STATEMENT

"SRETFEDEN CINSE EW EHVA
THEREFORE SINC(E) WE HAVE

EMBE YFIDEZISU GRUNTOM
BEEN JUSTIFIED THROUGH

THFIA EW EVHA CPEAE TIWH
FAITH WE HAVE (PEACE) WITH

ODG UTGHORH URO ROLD
GOD THROUGH OUR LORD

BVEJS RCITHA"
J(E)SUS (C)HRIST

ROMANS 5:1

I HAVE P(E)AC(E) WITH GOD

142

FILL IN THE BLANKS

WORD LIST	
BLAMELESS	SIGHT
WORLD	CREATION
HOLY	CHOSE

FOR HE C H O S E US IN HIM BEFORE
THE C R E A T I O N OF THE
W O R L D TO BE H O L Y AND
B L A M E L E S S IN HIS
S I G H T .

EPHESIANS 1:4

I AM ACCEPTED BY GOD!

143

UNSCRAMBLE THE VERSE

TO FIND OUT WHAT THE VERSE BELOW SAYS FILL IN THE BLANKS. ALL THE VOWELS ARE THERE SO ALL YOU NEED TO ADD ARE THE CONSONANTS.

YET TO ALL WHO
RECEIVE HIM TO THOSE
WHO BELIEVE IN HIS
NAME HE GAVE THE
RIGHT TO BECOME
CHILDREN OF GOD

JOHN 1:12

CHILD, BILLY! NOT BABY.

144

WORD SEARCH

FIND AND CIRCLE THE WORDS BELOW IN THE WORD SEARCH PUZZLE. LOOK UP, DOWN, FORWARD AND DIAGONALLY TO SOLVE THIS ONE!

PEACE
FAITH
RECEIVE
HOLY
ETERNAL

CHILDREN
CREATION
GOD
WORSHIP

145

LOOK-ALIKES

FIND AND CIRCLE TWELVE DIFFERENCES IN THE TWO PICTURES BELOW

146

FINISH THE VERSE

TO FIND OUT WHAT THE VERSE BELOW SAYS FILL IN THE BLANKS. ALL THE CONSONANTS ARE THERE SO ALL YOU NEED TO DO IS ADD THE VOWELS

VOWELS A E I O U

"DON'T YOU KNOW THAT
YOU YOURSELVES ARE
GOD'S TEMPLE AND THAT
GOD'S SPIRIT LIVES
IN YOU?

1 CORINTHIANS 3:16

I KNOW HE'S IN HERE SOMEWHERE. THERE'S GOTTA BE SOMETHING WRONG WITH YOUR PROGRAMMING!

WELL, I'LL KEEP LOOKING.

I HAVE THE HOLY SPIRIT INSIDE ME!

147

ZANY CODE BUSTER

USE THE CODE CHART BELOW TO DECODE THE MYSTERY VERSE

HMMMM THERE HAS TO BE A MORE PRACTICAL WAY!

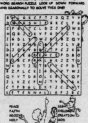

CONT'D ON THE NEXT PAGE

148

CONT'D FROM THE PREVIOUS PAGE

WHO GIVES
GENEROUSLY
TO ALL WITH
OUT FIND
FAULT
AND IT WILL
BE GIVEN
HIM.

MAYBE YOU SHOULD TRY THIS?

THAT DIDN'T FEEL TOO GOOD...

JAMES 1:5

I HAVE ACCESS TO GOD'S WISDOM!

149

TWICE THE FUN

UNSCRAMBLE THE UNDERLINED WORDS IN THE VERSE BELOW. THEN, ON THE NEXT PAGE, FIND AND CIRCLE THEM IN THE WORD SEARCH PUZZLE.

"LET US THEN APPROACH THE _ORENT_ OF GRACE WITH CONFIDENCE, SO THAT WE MAY RECEIVE _YRCEM_ AND FIND _EGACR_ TO HELP US IN OUR TIME OF _EDNE_."

<u>THRONE</u> <u>MERCY</u>

<u>GRACE</u> <u>NEED</u>

HEBREWS 4:16

I AM HELPED BY GOD!

CONT'D ON THE NEXT PAGE

150

CONT'D FROM THE PREVIOUS PAGE

```
S Q D W G L Z M
K T H R O N E G
F R N P Y C B A
A L H E A R F E
P X O R D J N R
R N G X F Q V C
I F P S N R D Y
N E E D R F P J
```

151

HIDDEN ALPHABET

FIND AND CIRCLE EVERY LETTER OF THE ALPHABET THAT HAS BEEN HIDDEN IN THIS PICTURE AND FINISH THE SENTENCE BELOW.

I RECEIVE M E R C Y BECAUSE OF GOD'S GRACE

152

AMAZING MAZES

FIND THE WAY TO THE THRONE OF GRACE

153

CODE BUSTER

USE THE CODE CHART BELOW TO COMPLETE THE VERSE. CHOOSE FROM THE LEFT SET OF NUMBERS FIRST (Eg. 23=Z)

	1	2	3	4	5	6
1	A	B	C	D	E	F
2	H	I	J	K	L	M
3	O	P	Q	R	S	T
4	V	W	X	Y	Z	

NOT ONLY IS THIS

SO, BUT WE ALSO

REJOICE IN GOD

THROUGH OUR LORD

JESUS CHRIST,

CONT'D ON THE NEXT PAGE

154

CONT'D FROM THE PREVIOUS PAGE

<u>THROUGH WHOM</u>

<u>WE HAVE NOW</u>

<u>RECEIVED</u>

<u>RECONCILIATION.</u>

ROMANS 5:11

HEY... WHAT IN THE WORLD DOES REC RECO RECON... WHATEVER MEAN?

"RECONCILE"? IT MEANS TO BE MADE FRIENDS WITH AGAIN

SO WE'RE MADE FRIENDS AGAIN WITH GOD!

COOL!

I AM RECONCILED TO GOD!

155

ZANY CODE BUSTER

TO DECODE THIS MYSTERY VERSE, LOOK AT EACH LETTER AND WRITE THE ONE THAT COMES BEFORE IT IN THE ALPHABET.

A B C D E F G H I J K L M N O P Q R S T U V W X Y Z

THEREFORE THERE
UIFSFGPSF UIFSF

IS NOW NO CONDEM
JT OPX OP DPOEFN

NATION FOR THOSE
OBUJPO GPS UIPTF

WHO
XIP

?!

CONT'D ON THE NEXT PAGE

156

CONT'D FROM THE PREVIOUS PAGE

ARE IN CHRIST
B S F J O D I S J T U

JESUS.
E F T V T

WHAT ABOUT CON-
DEM-NATION?
WHAT DOES
THAT MEAN?

ROMANS 8:1
TO BE
CONVICTED
AS GUILTY TO BE JUDGED
TO BE BLAMED ,CRITICIZED.
DOOMED, SIN

OKAY, OKAY!
I GET IT

WOW! THANKS TO
JESUS... THAT LL
NEVER HAPPEN
TO US!

WHY
COOLER
EVEN !

THERE IS NO CONDEMNATION FOR ME!

157

PICTURE FRAMES
WHAT COULD THE PICTURE BE??

DRAW EXACTLY WHAT IS IN EACH NUMBERED
FRAME AT THE TOP OF THE PAGE INTO EACH FRAME
OF THE SAME NUMBER IN THE GRID BELOW

THERE IS NO CONDEMNATION FOR
THOSE WHO ARE IN JESUS CHRIST!

158

• • DOT 2 DOT • •
CONNECT THE DOTS

THERE IS NO CONDEMNATION FOR
THOSE WHO ARE IN JESUS CHRIST!

159

FINISH THE VERSE
TO FIND OUT WHAT THE VERSE BELOW SAYS FILL
IN THE BLANKS ALL THE CONSONANTS ARE THERE
SO ALL YOU NEED TO DO IS ADD THE VOWELS

VOWELS A E I O U

BUT YOU WERE WASHED,

YOU WERE SANCTIFIED

YOU WERE JUSTIFIED

IN.

BEFORE YOU
EVEN ASK...
"JUSTIFIED"
MEANS TO
BE MADE
FREE FROM
GUILT OR
BLAME

I KNEW
THAT!

160

CONT'D FROM THE PREVIOUS PAGE

THE NAME OF THE

LORD JESUS CHRIST

AND BY THE SPIRIT OF

OUR GOD."

I CORINTHIANS 6:11

"...AND "SANCTIFIED"
MEANS TO BE
MADE HOLY!"

KNEW THAT
TOO !

EM-HUH !

I AM JUSTIFIED!

161

WORD SEARCH
CROSS OUT EVERY LETTER THAT APPEARS FOUR
TIMES IN THE PUZZLE TO FIND THE WORD THAT
COMPLETES THE SENTENCE

BECAUSE OF HIS GREAT L O V E FOR US
JESUS PAID THE PRICE FOR ALL OUR SINS!

162

LOOK-ALIKES
FIND AND CIRCLE TEN DIFFERENCES IN THE TWO
PICTURES BELOW

163

CODE BUSTER
USE THE CODE CHART BELOW TO COMPLETE THE
VERSE CHOOSE FROM THE LEFT SET OF NUMBERS
FIRST (Eg 23=7)

	1	2	3	4	5	6	7
1	A	B	C	D	E	F	G
2	H	I	J	K	E	L	M
3	O	P	Q	R	S	T	U
4	V	W	X	Y	Z		

"GOD MADE HIM WHO

HAD NO SIN TO BE

SIN FOR US SO

THAT IN HIM

CONT'D ON THE NEXT PAGE

164

CONT'D FROM THE PREVIOUS PAGE

WE MIGHT BECOME

THE RIGHTEOUS-

NESS OF GOD."

2 CORINTHIANS 5:21

JUST SO YOU KNOW...
"RIGHTEOUSNESS" ALSO
MEANS TO BE FREE OF
GUILT; TO BE SEEN
AS RIGHTEOUS IN
GOD'S EYES !

I HAVE HIS RIGHTEOUSNESS!

165

FILL IN THE BLANKS

"WE are therefore CHRIST'S AMBASSADORS as though GOD were making his APPEAL through US."

2 Corinthians 5:20

I AM GOD'S REPRESENTATIVE

166

TWICE THE FUN

Unscramble the underlined words in the verse below. Then on the next page find and circle them in the word search puzzle.

"IF WE CONFESS OUR SINS HE IS FAITHFUL and JUST and WILL FORGIVE US OUR SINS and PURIFY US FROM ALL UNRIGHTEOUSNESS."

CONFESS SINS
FAITHFUL JUST
FORGIVE PURIFY

1 John 1:9

168

...cont'd from the previous page

I HAVE TO ADMIT, THIS WAY IS BETTER.

I AM COMPLETELY FORGIVEN

169

ZANY CODE BUSTER

Use the code chart below to decode the mystery verse.

AND MY GOD WILL MEET ALL YOUR NEEDS

170

cont'd from the previous page

ACCORDING TO HIS GLORIOUS RICHES IN CHRIST JESUS

GOD...NEEDS MY BUD, NOT WANTS!

Philippians 4:19

I HAVE MY NEEDS MET BY GOD!

171

ZANY CODE BUSTER

To decode this mystery verse look at each letter and write the one that comes BEFORE it in the alphabet.

ABCDEFGHIJKLMNOPQR
STUVWXYZ

I HAVE LOVED YOU WITH AN EVERLASTING LOVE

Jeremiah 31:3

I AM TENDERLY LOVED!

174

UNSCRAMBLE THE VERSE

To find out what the verse below says, fill in the blanks. All the vowels are there so all you need to do is add the consonants.

"FOR WE ARE TO GOD THE AROMA OF CHRIST AMONG THOSE WHO ARE BEING SAVED AND THOSE WHO ARE PERISHING"

2 Corinthians 2:15

I AM A SWEET SMELL OF CHRIST TO GOD!

175

FINISH THE VERSE

To find out what the verse below says, fill in the blanks. All the consonants are there so all you need to do is add the vowels.

VOWELS: A E I O U

"FOR WE ARE THE TEMPLE OF THE LIVING GOD."

2 Corinthians 6:16

YOU KNOW, HAKEEM... WE REALLY NEED TO TALK...

I AM THE TEMPLE OF GOD!

176

CODE BUSTER

Use the code chart below to complete the verse. Choose from the left set of numbers first. (Eg. 23=J)

"BUT NOW HE HAS RECONCILED YOU BY CHRIST'S PHYSICAL BODY"

cont'd on the next page

177

CONT'D FROM THE PREVIOUS PAGE

THROUGH DEATH

TO PRESENT YOU

HOLY IN HIS SIGHT,

WITHOUT BLEMISH

AND FREE FROM

ACCUSATION."

I CAN'T SEEM TO FIND MY CHOCO- CANDY-CARAMEL- FRUITY-BEAR PLAYS... COLOSSIANS 1:22

WELL, AH-MMMM, DON'T BLAME ME.

I AM BLAMELESS AND BEYOND REPROACH!

178

ZANY CODE BUSTER

USE THE CODE CHART BELOW TO DECODE THE MYSTERY VERSE

"BUT SEEK

HIS KINGDOM

AND THESE

THINGS WILL

BE GIVEN

TO YOU

AS WELL."

LUKE 12:31

I WILL TALK TO GOD EVERY DAY

180

UNSCRAMBLE THE VERSE

TO FIND OUT WHAT THE VERSE BELOW SAYS FILL IN THE BLANKS. ALL THE VOWELS ARE THERE SO ALL YOU NEED TO ADD ARE THE CONSONANTS

"MMTOC URSO SNHA OT EHT BOBL, UTRRS NE DHS DHN SH LLWL, EAKA ROYU TEBHORSRUOGN NEHSS ESLL HET VOWL."

"COMMIT YOUR WAYS TO

THE LORD TRUST IN

HIM AND HE WILL

MAKE YOUR RIGHTEOUS-

NESS SHINE LIKE THE

DAWN." PSALM 37:56

I WILL COMMIT MY WAYS TO THE LORD

181

FINISH THE VERSE

TO FIND OUT WHAT THE VERSE BELOW SAYS FILL IN THE BLANKS. ALL THE CONSONANTS ARE THERE SO ALL YOU NEED TO DO IS ADD THE VOWELS

VOWELS: A E I O U

"THIS IS THE DAY THE

LORD HAS MADE. LET

US REJOICE AND BE

GLAD IN IT."

PSALMS 118:24

I WILL MAKE TODAY MY REST DAY

184

CODE BUSTER

USE THE CODE CHART BELOW TO COMPLETE THE VERSE. CHOOSE FROM THE LEFT SET OF NUMBERS FIRST (Eg 13=J)

	1	2	3	4	5	6	7
1	A	B	C	D	E	F	G
2	H	I	J	K	L	M	N
3	O	P	Q	R	S	T	U
4	V	W	X	Y	Z		

WHATEVER

HAPPENS, CONDUCT

YOURSELVES IN A

MANNER WORTHY OF

THE GOSPEL OF

CHRIST.

PHILIPPIANS 1:27

185

TWICE THE FUN

UNSCRAMBLE THE UNDERLINED WORDS IN THE VERSE BELOW THEN ON THE NEXT PAGE FIND AND CIRCLE THEM IN THE WORD SEARCH PUZZLE.

"BE KIDN AND COMPASSIONATE TO EACH ANOTHER FORGIVING EACH OTHER, STUJ AS IN RHSIEC GOD FRAGVOE YOU."

KIND ONE JUST

CHRIST FORGAVE

EPHESIANS 4:32

CONT'D ON THE NEXT PAGE

186

...CONT'D FROM THE PREVIOUS PAGE.

I WILL BE KIND TO OTHERS

187

PICTURE FRAMES

WHAT COULD THE PICTURE BE?

DRAW EXACTLY WHAT IS IN EACH NUMBERED FRAME AT THE TOP OF THE PAGE INTO EACH FRAME OF THE SAME NUMBER IN THE GRID BELOW

188

ZANY CODE BUSTER

TO DECODE THIS MYSTERY VERSE, LOOK AT EACH LETTER AND WRITE THE ONE THAT COMES BEFORE IT IN THE ALPHABET

A B C D E F G H I J K L M N O P Q R S T U V W X Y Z

"I CAN DO EVERY

THING THROUGH

HIM WHO GIVES ME

STRENGTH"

PHILIPPIANS 4:13

I WILL DO WHAT I'M ASKED WITHOUT COMPLAINT

189

UNSCRAMBLE THE VERSE

TO FIND OUT WHAT THE VERSE BELOW SAYS, FILL
IN THE BLANKS. ALL THE VOWELS ARE THERE SO
ALL YOU NEED TO ADD ARE THE CONSONANTS.

"B_ V_RY C_R_F_L, ET_N, W_O _UR EV_L - T_N _A
WU_S_N TU_ _A EIW_ A_E_A_ H_T T_N_ PO
_V_RY NT_VU_TT_PO _A_G_LU_ _TH _O_A _A_ LIV_"

B_ V_RY C_R_F_L.

_H_N H_W Y_U LIV_.

N_T A_ _NW_S_ B_T A_

W_S_ M_K_NG T_H_

M_ST _F _V_RY _PP_R.

T_N_TY B_C_US_ T_H_

D_Y_ _R_ _V_L.

EPHESIANS 5.15-16

I WILL MAKE THE MOST OF EVERY
OPPORTUNITY

190

MULTIPLE CHOICE

CIRCLE THE CORRECT ANSWER

1 WE SHOULD PUT OUR TRUST IN
   A MONEY
   B THE LORD
   C FRIENDS

2 WHAT MUST WE SEEK TO BE GIVEN ALL
   THINGS?
   A A JOB
   B A RAISE IN OUR ALLOWANCE
   C GOD'S KINGDOM

3 EVERYONE WHO HAS WILL BE GIVEN
   MATTHEW 25.29
   A REALLY COOL SIZE
   MORE, AND HE WILL HAVE
   AN ABUNDANCE
   B NOTHING YOUR ROOM'S TOO
   CROWDED ANYWAYS
   C SMALL PIG

I WILL USE MY TALENTS EVERY DAY

191

ZANY CODE BUSTER

USE THE CODE CHART BELOW TO DECODE THE
MYSTERY VERSE

(code chart grid)

A N D   W E   K N O W
...

CONT'D ON THE NEXT PAGE...

192

CONT'D FROM THE PREVIOUS PAGE

T H E   G O O D   O F
T H O S E   W H O
L O V E   H I M . W H O
H A V E   B E E N
C A L L E D
A C C O R D I N G   T O
H I S   P U R
P O S E

ROMANS 8.28

I WILL TRUST GOD TO WORK EVERYTHING OUT

193

FILL IN THE BLANKS

WORD LIST	
HELPFUL	BENEFIT
NEEDS	UNWHOLESOME
ACCORDING	LISTEN
TALK	MOUTHS

"DO NOT LET ANY U N W H O L E -

S O M E   T A L K COME OUT OF YOUR

M O U T H S , BUT ONLY WHAT IS

H E L P F U L FOR BUILDING OTHERS

UP

HEY...
YA' DOIN'
THOSE 'WEIRD'
DRAWINGS
AGAIN?

CONT'D ON THE NEXT PAGE...

194

CONT'D FROM THE PREVIOUS PAGE.

A C C O R D I N G TO THEIR

N E E D S THAT IT MAY B E N E -

F I T THOSE WHO L I S T E N -

EPHESIANS 4.29

I'M REALLY SORRY,
LIL' BRO'... I WAS THE
ONE BEING 'STUPID'! I
GUESS... I WAS...

A LITTLE JEALOUS
I JUST WISH I
COULD DRAW AS
GOOD AS YOU...
YOU'RE 'THE BEST!'

I WILL ENCOURAGE OTHERS TO BE ALL GOD
CREATED THEM TO BE

195

CODE BUSTER

USE THE CODE CHART BELOW TO COMPLETE THE
VERSE. CHOOSE FROM THE LEFT SET OF NUMBERS
FIRST (Eg B3=J)

	1	2	3	4	5	6	7
A	A	B	C	D	E	F	G
M	H	I	J	K	L	M	N
X	O	P	Q	R	S	T	U
V	V	W	X	Y	Z		

D O   N O T   B E   A N X I O U S

A B O U T   A N Y T H I N G

B U T   I N   E V E R Y T H I N G .

B Y   P R A Y E R

CONT'D ON THE NEXT PAGE...

196

CONT'D FROM THE PREVIOUS PAGE.

A N D   P E T I T I O N   W I T H

T H A N K S G I V I N G

P R E S E N T   Y O U R

R E Q U E S T S   T O   G O D .

PHILIPPIANS 4.6

DON'T PANIC...
THIS IS
SUPPOSED TO
BE FUN!

I WILL NOT PANIC...I WILL PRAY

197

SEE YA' NEXT TIME!

You're in for the ultimate
American Adventure!
Collect all 48 books!